Nelson Mathematics 4

Teacher's Resource

Chapter 11: 3-D Geometry and 3-D Measurement

Series Authors and Senior Consultants
Mary Lou Kestell • Marian Small

Senior Authors
Heather Kelleher • Kathy Kubota-Zarivnij • Pat Milot
Betty Morris • Doug Super

Teacher's Resource Chapter Authors
Gail May • Debbie Sturgeon

Assessment Consultant
Damian Cooper

THOMSON
NELSON

Australia   Canada   Mexico   Singapore   Spain   United Kingdom   United States

THOMSON

NELSON

**Nelson Mathematics 4
Teacher's Resource**

**Series Authors and
Senior Consultants**
Mary Lou Kestell, Marian Small

Senior Authors
Heather Kelleher,
Kathy Kubota-Zarivnij, Pat Milot,
Betty Morris, Doug Super

Authors
Carol Brydon, Anne Cirillo,
Andrea Dickson, Roz Doctorow,
Wendy Dowling, Catharine Gilmour,
Elizabeth Grill-Donovan,
Jack Hope, Wendy Klassen,
Kathy Kubota-Zarivnij,
David Leach, Pat Margerm,
Gail May, Pat Milot,
Scott Sincerbox, Marian Small,
Mary Steele, Susan Stuart,
Debbie Sturgeon, Rosita Tseng Tam

Assessment Consultant
Damian Cooper

Director of Publishing
David Steele

Publisher, Mathematics
Beverley Buxton

Senior Program Manager
Shirley Barrett

**Teacher's Resource
Program Managers**
Janice Nixon
Alan Simpson
David Spiegel

Developmental Editors
Janice Barr
Julie Bedford
Colin Bisset
Jenna Dunlop
James Gladstone
Adrienne Mason
Margaret McClintock
Janice Nixon
Frances Purslow
Mary Reeve
Elizabeth Salomons
Tom Shields
Alan Simpson
Michael Tabor

Editorial Assistant
Megan Robinson

**Executive Managing Editor,
Development & Testing**
Cheryl Turner

**Executive Managing Editor,
Production**
Nicola Balfour

Production Editor
Sheila Stephenson

Copy Editor
Margaret Allen

Senior Production Coordinator
Sharon Latta Paterson

Production Coordinator
Franca Mandarino

Creative Director
Angela Cluer

Art Director
Ken Phipps

Art Management
ArtPlus Ltd., Suzanne Peden

Illustrators
ArtPlus Ltd.

Interior and Cover Design
Suzanne Peden

Cover Image
Corbis/Magna

**ArtPlus Ltd. Production
Coordinator**
Dana Lloyd

Composition
Lynn Serson/ArtPlus Ltd.

**Photo Research and
Permissions**
Vicki Gould

Printer
Webcom

COPYRIGHT © 2004 by Nelson,
a division of Thomson Canada
Limited.

Printed and bound in Canada
2 3 4 08 07 06

For more information contact
Nelson, 1120 Birchmount Road,
Toronto, Ontario, M1K 5G4. Or
you can visit our Internet site at
http://www.nelson.com

**National Library of Canada
Cataloguing in Publication**

Nelson mathematics 4.
Teacher's resource /
Mary Lou Kestell ... [et al.].

ISBN 0-17-620183-1

1. Mathematics—Study and
teaching (Elementary)
I. Kestell, Mary Lou
II. Title: Nelson mathematics four.

QA135.6.N444 2003 Suppl. 3
510   C2003-904835-7

3-D Geometry and 3-D Measurement

Contents

Introduction

This chapter extends students' work from Grade 3 in 3-D geometry and measurement.

In geometry, students will
- solve problems involving 3-D shapes
- examine the 2-D faces of 3-D shapes to talk about their similarities and differences
- sketch the faces of 3-D shapes
- design and make skeletons of 3-D shapes
- discuss geometric ideas and how these ideas are used in our everyday lives

In measurement, students will
- select appropriate units of capacity or mass
- order objects by mass using grams and kilograms
- relate grams to kilograms and millilitres to litres

Strategy Focus: Using Mathematical Language
Lesson 5 focuses on the importance of using accurate and descriptive mathematical language to describe 3-D shapes and to describe mathematical reasoning about properties of the shapes.

Curriculum Across Grades 3 to 5: 3-D Geometry and 3-D Measurement

All the Grade 4 expectations listed below are covered in this chapter.
When the expectation is a focus of a particular lesson, the lesson number is indicated in brackets.

Grade 3	Grade 4	Grade 5
Overall Expectations: **Measurement** • demonstrate an understanding of and ability to apply measurement terms: millilitre, litre, gram, kilogram • identify relationships between and among measurement concepts • solve problems related to their day-to-day environment using measurement and estimation • estimate, measure, and record the capacity of containers and the mass of familiar objects, and compare the measures **Geometry and Spatial Sense** • investigate the attributes of three-dimensional figures using concrete materials and drawings • draw and build three-dimensional objects and models • use language effectively to describe geometric concepts, reasoning, and investigation	**Overall Expectations:** **Measurement** • demonstrate an understanding of and ability to apply appropriate metric prefixes in measurement and estimation activities (**6**, **7**) • identify relationships between and among measurement concepts (**7**, **8**) • solve problems related to their day-to-day environment using measurement and estimation (**7**, **8**) • estimate, measure, and record the capacity of containers and the mass of familiar objects, compare the measures, and model the volume of three-dimensional figures (**6**, **7**, **8**, **9**) **Geometry and Spatial Sense** • solve problems using geometric models • investigate the attributes of three-dimensional figures and two-dimensional shapes using concrete materials and drawings (**1, 2, 3**) • draw and build three-dimensional objects and models (**2, 3, 4**) • use language effectively to describe geometric concepts, reasoning, and investigations (**2, 5**)	**Overall Expectations:** **Measurement** • demonstrate an understanding of and ability to apply appropriate metric prefixes in measurement and estimation activities • estimate, measure, and record the capacity of containers, the mass of familiar objects, and the volume of irregular three-dimensional figures, and compare the measures **Geometry and Spatial Sense** • identify, describe, compare, and classify geometric figures • draw and build three-dimensional objects and models • use mathematical language effectively to describe geometric concepts, reasoning, and investigations
Specific Expectations: **Capacity, Volume, Mass** • estimate, measure, and record the capacity of containers using standard units (millilitre, litre) and compare the measures • estimate, measure, and record the mass of familiar objects using standard units (gram, kilogram)	**Specific Expectations:** **Capacity, Volume, Mass** • select the most appropriate standard unit to measure the capacity of containers (**7, 8**) • estimate, measure, and record the mass of objects using standard units compare the measures, and order objects by mass (**6**) • model three-dimensional figures of specific volumes using blocks (**9**) • describe the relationship between grams and kilograms and millilitres and litres (**8**) • select the most appropriate standard unit to measure mass (e.g., milligram or gram) (**8**)	**Specific Expectations:** **Capacity, Volume, Mass** • measure containers by volume using standard units: cubic centimetres • determine the relationship between capacity and volume by measuring the volume of various objects and by determining the displacement of liquid by each object • relate the volume of an irregular three-dimensional figures to its capacity • describe the relationships between millilitres and cubic centimetres • determine the relationship between kilograms and metric tonnes • select the most appropriate standard unit to measure mass
Three- and Two-Dimensional Geometry • investigate the similarities and differences among a variety of prisms using concrete materials and drawings • build rectangular prisms from given nets and explore the attributes of the prisms • use two-dimensional shapes to make a three-dimensional model using a variety of building materials • sketch a picture of a structure or model created from three-dimensional figures • compare and sort three-dimensional figures according to two or more geometric attributes • describe and name prisms and pyramids by the shape of their base • explain the process they followed in making a structure from three-dimensional figures • match and describe congruent (identical) three-dimensional figures	**Three- and Two-Dimensional Geometry** • identify the two-dimensional shapes of the faces of three-dimensional figures (**1, 2, 4**) • sketch the faces that make up a three-dimensional figure using concrete materials as models (**1**) • design and make skeletons for three-dimensional figures (**3**) • use mathematical language to describe geometric ideas (**5**) • recognize and describe the occurrence and application of geometric properties and principles in the everyday world • discuss geometric concepts with peers and explain their understanding of the concepts (**3, 5**) • discuss ideas, make connections, and articulate hypotheses about geometric properties and relationships (**1, 3**)	**Three- and Two-Dimensional Geometry** • identify nets for a variety of polyhedra from drawings while holding three-dimensional figures in their hands • construct nets of cubes and pyramids using a variety of materials • construct a figure with interlocking cubes that matches a picture of the figure • sketch the faces that make up a three-dimensional figure by looking at a three-dimensional figure

Math Background: Research and Important Issues

Geometry: The first part of the chapter focuses on 3-D geometry. There is a significant amount of work on determining the numbers of vertices, edges, and faces in a shape to describe the shape's properties. A general formula about 3-D shapes, called Euler's theorum, is brought out in the feature Curious Math after Lesson 1. Euler's theorum states that in any polyhedron, the number of faces added to the number of vertices is 2 greater than the number of edges − E + F = 2). For example, in a triangle-based prism, there are 5 faces, 6 vertices and 9 edges.

For pyramids the number of faces with an n-sided base is $n + 1$, the number of vertices is $n + 1$, and the number of edges is $2n$. If $n = 4$, then the number of faces is 5, the number of vertices is 5, and the number of edges is 8.

Measurement: Students often have less experience working with 3-D measurement (capacity and mass) than with length or area. Although students in earlier grades are exposed to the independence of capacity and mass, many still believe that something that holds more is heavier.

Students area also introduced to volume, another 3-D measure. Although capacity defines the amount something holds and volume defines the amount needed to build something, the two measures are often confused. For example, the capacity of a truck is measured in cubic metres (volume) rather than litres (capacity). Later on, students will learn the relationship between volume and capacity units, but for now, it is helpful to talk about how much something holds (capacity) in contrast to how much material it takes to create something (volume).

Planning for Instruction

Problem Solving

- Assign a Problem of the Week each week from the selection below (see p. 76 for sample answers) or from your own collection.
  1. Choose 3 objects from the classroom, and describe each one by including the number of vertices, edges, and faces.
  2. Describe the shape of your school building, by drawing and labelling the attributes. Write about the shape of the roof, as well as the rest of the building. Explain your thinking.
  3. Find and record the total mass of the objects in your desk. Edit your work, using the Communication Checklist on page 303 in the student text.
- Create a poster to keep track of problem-solving strategies used in the chapter. You could put a checkmark beside the strategies that students find most useful.

Connections to Literature

Expand your classroom library or math centre with books related to the math in this chapter. For example,

Block City (Robert L. Stevenson, Dutton, 1988)

Counting on Frank (Rod Clement, Gareth Stevens Publishing, 1991)

Incredible Cross Sections (Stephen Biesty, Knopf, 1992)

Is a Blue Whale the Biggest Thing There Is? (Robert E. Wells, Albert Whitman & Company, 1993)

Mr. Archimedes Bath (Pamela Allen, Harper Collins Publishers, reprint, 1991)

Round Buildings, Square Buildings and Buildings That Wiggle Like a Fish (Philip Isaacson, Knopf, 1988)

Who Sank the Boat? (Pamela Allen, Coward-McCann Inc, 1990)

Connections to Other Math Strands

Number Operations: Although the formula for volume is not introduced in this chapter, the informal introduction refers to three dimensions, and many students will make the connection that the "number of cubic units" can be determined by multiplying length times width times height.

Place Value: The metric measuring system provides meaningful contexts for understanding multiples of 10, such as grams and kilograms, millilitres and litres, as well as tenths and decimals (e.g., 3.5 L equals 3500 mL).

Data Management: Students count or measure, and record data related to attributes of 3-D shapes, as well as mass and capacity, throughout this unit.

Connections to Other Curricula

Social Studies: In the lessons on 3-D shapes, students describe and compare the attributes of a variety of buildings. This provides meaningful contexts in which to discuss the relationship between form and function, as well as materials used in the built environment.

Art: In Lesson 4, students learn about drawing 3-D shapes with perspective, using techniques such as parallel lines, vanishing points, and shadows.

Language Arts: In Lesson 5, students write a rough copy then use a Communication Checklist to edit and revise their work.

Connections to Home and Community

- Throughout the unit, students refer to 3-D shapes in the natural and built environment. They describe buildings as well as objects from school and home. These activities could be connected with Social Studies and Art, through community walks where students observe, draw, and describe (using math language) the natural and human-made objects in their community.
- Students will benefit from observing a building under construction so that they can see how a building's 2 by 4 frame makes *edges* and how plywood sheets make *faces* in structures.
- Send home the Family Newsletter (Master on p. 62).
- Have students complete the *Mathematics 4 Workbook* pages for this chapter at home.
- Use the At Home suggestions found in most lessons.

Chapter 11 Planning Chart

Key Concepts

Shapes of different dimensions and their properties can be described mathematically. There are many representations of 2-D and 3-D shapes.
Any shape can be created by either combining or dissecting other shapes.
2-D and 3-D shapes can be located in space. They can be relocated or reoriented using mathematical procedures.
Some attributes of objects can be described using measurements.

The numerical value attached to a measurement is relative to the measurement unit. The unit must be used repeatedly to determine the measure.
Standard units, estimates, and measurement formulas are used to simplify communication about or calculation of measurements.
Tools, units of measure, and degree of precision must be appropriate to the purpose and content.

Student Book Section	Lesson Goal	ON Expectations	Pacing 13 days	Prerequisite Skills/Concepts
Getting Started: Describing Packages, pp. 292–293 (TR pp. 10–12)	Use concepts and skills developed prior to this chapter.		1 day	• Recognize basic 2-D and 3-D shapes. • Estimate, measure, and record the capacity of containers and the mass of objects. • Compare the measures using the appropriate terms: millilitre, litre, gram, kilogram.
Lesson 1: Exploration Sketching Faces, p. 294 (TR pp. 13–15)	Describe relationships between 3-D shapes and their 2-D faces.	4m62, 4m68, 4m69, 4m80	1 day	• Recognize basic 2-D and 3-D shapes. • Recognize and count faces and edges of 3-D shapes.
Lesson 2: Exploration Building 3-D Shapes with Congruent Faces, p. 296 (TR pp. 17–19)	Build 3-D shapes and describe relationships between faces and vertices.	4m62, 4m63, 4m67, 4m68	1 day	• Identify the face, vertex/vertices, and sides of 2-D shapes (squares and triangles). • Use nets to construct 3-D shapes.
Lesson 3: Exploration Making Skeleton Models, pp. 298–299 (TR pp. 21–24)	Build 3-D skeletons and describe relationships between edges and vertices.	4m62, 4m63, 4m70, 4m79, 4m80	1 day	• Describe the attributes of 3-D figures and 2-D shapes. • Use language effectively to describe geometric concepts, reasoning, and investigations.
Lesson 4: Direct Instruction Drawing 3-D Shapes, pp. 300–301 (TR pp. 25–28)	Draw prisms and pyramids.	4m63, 4m68	1 day	• Identify faces, vertices, and edges of 3-D shapes by name. • Identify and discriminate between a pyramid and a prism.
Lesson 5: Guided Activity Communicate an Understanding of Geometric Concepts, pp. 302–303 (TR pp. 29–32)	Use math language to show what you know about a 3-D shape.	4m67, 4m77, 4m79	1 day	• Identify the attributes of triangular prisms and pyramids. • Construct skeleton models of 3-D shapes. • Use writing terms *rough copy* and *good copy.*
Lesson 6: Exploration Measuring Mass, p. 305 (TR pp. 35–38)	Estimate, measure, and record the mass of objects.	4m34, 4m38, 4m58	1 day	• Use a balance scale to compare relative mass of two objects. • Use estimation to compare sums of numbers to a target rounded number. • Use rounding to tens and hundreds places.
Lesson 7: Exploration Measuring Capacity, pp. 306–307 (TR pp. 39–42)	Estimate, measure, and record the capacity of containers.	4m34, 4m35, 4m36, 4m38, 4m56	1 day	• Recognize when to apply measurement terms *millilitre* and *litre.* • Understand how the shape of the container may influence estimated volume.
Lesson 8: Guided Activity Using Mass and Capacity, pp. 308–309 (TR pp. 43–46)	Choose appropriate capacity and mass units.	4m35, 4m36, 4m38, 4m56, 4m59, 4m60	1 day	• Estimate, measure, and record the mass of objects. • Estimate, measure, and record the capacity of containers.
Lesson 9: Guided Activity Modelling Volume, pp. 310–311 (TR pp. 47–50)	Model 3-D shapes to measure volume.	4m38, 4m57	1 day	• Identify rows and columns in 2-D grids and 3-D prisms. • Identify a 3-D shape, viewed from more than one perspective, as the same shape. • Identify length, width, and height.
Curious Math: p. 295 (TR p. 16) **Mental Imagery:** p. 297 (TR p. 20) **Curious Math:** p. 299 (TR p. 24) **Mid-Chapter Review:** p. 304 (TR pp. 33–34) **Cumulative Review:** p. 319 (TR pp. 60–61)	**Skills Bank:** pp. 312–313 (TR pp. 51–52) **Problem Bank:** pp. 314–315 (TR p. 53) **Chapter Review:** pp. 316–317 (TR pp. 54–57) **Chapter Task:** p. 318 (TR pp. 58–59)		3 days	

Chapter Goals

Draw, build, and describe 3-dimensional (3-D) shapes.
Describe attributes of 3-D shapes.
Estimate, measure, and compare the volume, capacity, and mass of 3-D shapes.
Make connections between 2-D and 3-D geometry and between geometry and measurement.

Materials	Masters/ Workbook	Extra Practice and Extension in the Student Book
variety of packages of different sizes, shapes, and masses (2 packages/student) (optional) ruler, measuring tape, balance scales, and masses	1 cm Grid Paper, Masters Booklet, p. 23 (for Extra Support) Scaffolding p. 69 (for Assessment) Initial Assessment Summary, Masters Booklet, p. 1	
variety of prisms and pyramids (minimum of one/student)	Mental Math Master p. 63 3-D Shapes and 2-D Faces Master p. 72 Workbook p. 94	Mid-Chapter Review Questions 1 & 2 Skills Bank Question 1 Problem Bank Question 1 Chapter Review Questions 1 & 2
3-D shapes, such as cubes, pyramids, or prisms construction paper equilateral triangles, 30/group construction paper squares, 16/group scissors, roll of tape, 1/group	Mental Math Master p. 63 1 cm Square Dot Paper, Masters Booklet, p. 25 Triangle Dot Paper, Masters Booklet, p. 26 3-D Shapes Chart p. 73 Workbook p. 95	Mid-Chapter Review Questions 2 & 4 Skills Bank Question 2 Problem Bank Question 2 Chapter Review Questions 1, 2, & 3
toothpicks, 50/pair of students modelling clay (for Extra Challenge) bamboo skewers	Mental Math Master p. 63 Workbook p. 96	Mid-Chapter Review Question 3 Skills Bank Question 3 Problem Bank Questions 3, 4, & 5 Chapter Review Question 3
pattern square and pattern block triangle, 1/student ruler, 1/student circular counter, 1/student dice, 2/pair of students	Mental Math Master p. 63 (optional) Triangle Dot Paper, Masters Booklet, p. 26 Workbook p. 97	Mid-Chapter Review Question 4 Skills Bank Question 4 Chapter Review Question 4
toothpicks, 10/small group of students 1 ball of modelling clay/small group of students	Mental Math Master p. 63 (for Extra Support) Scaffolding Master p. 71 Workbook p. 98	Chapter Review Question 5
1 kg sugar, 500 g box of cereal, 5 g salt balance scale and masses/small group of students	Mental Math Master p. 64 List of Food and Clothing Master p. 74 Workbook p. 99	Skills Bank Questions 5 Problem Bank Questions 6, 7, 8, & 9 Chapter Review Questions 6 & 7
1-L bottle and 250 mL measuring cup/small group of students a variety of other containers including a drinking glass and a mug water funnel, 1/small group of students	Mental Math Master p. 64 Workbook p. 100	Skills Bank Question 6 Problem Bank Question 10 Chapter Review Question 8
plastic grocery bag several canned and boxed food items to add up to a total of 1 kg (optional) balance scales/small group of students (optional) set of measuring spoons and cups/small group of students	Mental Math Master p. 64 Workbook p. 101	Skills Bank Questions 7, 8, & 9 Problem Bank Question 11 Chapter Review Question 9
set of linking cubes/small group of students (optional) a variety of rectangle-based prisms and square-based prisms (optional) string	Mental Math Master p. 64 Workbook p. 102	Skills Bank Questions 10 & 11 Chapter Review Question 10
Curious Math: 2 prisms, 2 pyramids, (optional) calculator **Mental Imagery:** modelling clay and dental floss/small group of students **Curious Math:** (optional) skeleton shape from Lesson 3, flashlight or table lamp	Chapter 11 Test Masters 1 & 2 pp. 65–66 Chapter 11 Task Masters 1 & 2 pp. 67–68 Workbook p. 103	

Planning for Assessment

The Chapter 11 Assessment Chart on the next page lists many opportunities for assessment using a variety of strategies: written questions, short answer, investigation, observation and product marking. To guide you, refer to the recording tools and samples provided in the Masters Booklet pages 1 to 14.

Managing Initial Assessment

- To see the specific assessment suggestions for Getting Started, refer to pages 10 to 12 in this booklet. This initial assessment opportunity includes the exploratory activity Describing Packages and 5 skills-based questions in Do You Remember?
- You may use other initial assessments involving informal interview or written questions; for example, your own diagnostic activity.
- Use *Initial Assessment Summary* (Tool 1) to help you record your observations and concerns about the prior knowledge that an individual brings to Chapter 11. You may choose to record observations for all students, or for only those individuals who appear to have difficulty.

Managing Assessment for Feedback

- To see the specific assessment suggestions for Lessons 1 to 9, refer to the second column of the Chapter 11 Assessment Chart on the next page.
- You may use other informal feedback assessments involving ongoing observations and interviews to help you adapt your instruction to suit the needs of individual students.
- Use any of these tools to help you improve student achievement:
  What to Look for When Assessing Student Achievement (Tool 2),
  Coaching Students Towards Success (Tool 3),
  Student Interview Form (with prompts) (Tool 4),
  Student Interview Form (without prompts) (Tool 5).
- **Peer Assessment:** As students are working together, encourage them to listen to one another and assist if appropriate. Good opportunities for informal peer assessment occur in the Exploration Lessons 1, 2, 3, 6, and 7, and the Communication strategy Lesson 5.
- **Self Assessment:** As students are working through the chapter, encourage them to practise at home. They can use the Skills Bank or the Workbook.
- **Journal Writing:** Good opportunities for journal writing occur in the Reflecting or Consolidation section in any lesson.

Managing Assessment of Learning

- Refer to the last 4 columns of the Chapter 11 Assessment Chart on the next page. There you will find detailed support for all the Key Assessment Questions in Lessons 1 to 9, and all of the questions in the Mid-Chapter Review and Chapter Review, as well as the Chapter 3 Task. Which of these opportunities you choose to assess will depend on the quantity of evidence you need to gather for individual students.

  Note: When charts show levels of student achievement, they are always based on the appropriate parts of the 4 generic rubrics (scoring scales):
  Problem Solving Rubric (Tool 6),
  Understanding of Concepts Rubric (Tool 7),
  Application of Procedures Rubric (Tool 8),
  Communication Rubric (Tool 9).
- If you want to assess other questions from the lessons, the Problem Bank, or the Problems of the Week, use the appropriate rows from the 4 generic rubrics to create your own question-specific rubric.
- Use any of these tools to help you record and track student achievement:
  Assessment of Learning Summary—Individual Student (Tool 10),
  Assessment of Learning Summary—Class by Strand (Tool 11).
- **Self Assessment:** After students have completed the chapter, encourage them to try Test Yourself on Workbook page 103. (Answers to these multiple choice and all other Workbook questions can be found at **www.mathk8.nelson.com**.)
- **Journal Writing:** A good opportunity for journal writing occurs in Consolidation in Lesson 2 when students answer the prompt "What have you learned about the relationships between faces and vertices of 3-D shapes that are made from congruent faces?" and in the Chapter Review where students reflect on the chapter's goal.

Managing Chapter Evaluation

- Look at the assessment data you've recorded throughout the chapter on Tools 10 and 11. Also include any end-of-chapter information from either the Chapter 11 Task Pages 1 & 2 pp. 67-68 or the Chapter 11 Test Pages 1 & 2 pp. 65–66. Determine the most consistent level for an individual.

Chapter 11 Assessment Chart

Student Book Lesson	Assessment for Feedback Chart	Assessment of Learning			
		Chart	Question/Category	ON Expectations	Strategy
Lesson 1: Exploration Sketching Faces, p. 294	TR p. 13	TR p. 15	all, Problem Solving	4m62, 4m68, 4m69, 4m80	investigation
Lesson 2: Exploration Building 3-D Shapes with Congruent Faces, p. 296	TR p. 17	TR p. 19	all, Problem Solving	4m62, 4m63, 4m67, 4m68	investigation
Lesson 3: Exploration Making Skeleton Models, pp. 298–299	TR p. 21	TR p. 24	all, Problem Solving	4m62, 4m63, 4m70, 4m79, 4m80	investigation
Lesson 4: Direct Instruction Drawing 3-D Shapes, pp. 300–301	TR p. 25	TR p. 28	6, Application of Procedures	4m63, 4m68	short answer
Lesson 5: Guided Activity Communicate an Understanding of Geometric Concepts, pp. 302–303	TR p. 29	TR p. 32	4, Communication	4m67, 4m77, 4m79	short answer
Mid-Chapter Review, p. 304		TR p. 34–35	1, Understanding of Concepts, Application of Procedures	4m62	written question
			2, Understanding of Concepts, Communication	4m73	written question
			3, Application of Procedures	4m70	short answer
			4, Problem Solving	4m80	written question
Lesson 6: Exploration Measuring Mass, p. 305	TR p. 35	TR p. 38	all, Problem Solving	4m34, 4m38, 4m58	investigation
Lesson 7: Exploration Measuring Capacity, pp. 306–307	TR p. 39	TR p. 42	all, Problem Solving	4m34, 4m35, 4m36, 4m38, 4m56	investigation
Lesson 8: Guided Activity Using Mass and Capacity, pp. 308–309	TR p. 43	TR p. 46	7, Understanding of Concepts	4m35, 4m36, 4m38, 4m56, 4m59, 4m60	short answer
Lesson 9: Guided Activity Modelling Volume, pp. 310–311	TR p. 47	TR p. 50	5, Application of Procedures	4m38, 4m57	short answer
Chapter Review, pp. 316–317		TR pp. 55–56	1, Problem Solving	4m63, 4m73	written question
			2, Communication	4m68, 4m73	written question
			3, Application of Procedures, Understanding of Concepts	4m62, 4m68	written question
			4, Application of Procedures	4m70	written question
			5, Communication	4m67, 4m70	written question
			6, Problem Solving	4m58	written question
			7, Understanding of Concepts	4m58, 4m50	short answer
			8, Application of Procedures	4m58, 4m50	short answer
			9, Understanding of Concepts	4m41	short answer
			10, Application of Procedures	4m57	short answer
Chapter Task, p. 318		TR p. 59	entire task, Problem Solving	4m50, 4m57, 4m59, 4m63, 4m78	observation and product marking
Cumulative Review, Chapters 8–11, pp. 319–320		TR p. 60–61			

Reading Strategies

Reading for Understanding	Strategies
Getting Started **Building a mathematical vocabulary:** Students will have a better understanding of instructional terms.	• Have students explain what is meant by "describe" and "compare." • Ask students to check their explanation against the Glossary for Instructional Words. • Ask students why it is important to be able to describe and compare in math.
Lesson 1 **Using text features to help understand the text:** Students will be able to find the meaning of words written in bold text by using the glossary.	• Ask students to identify the words written in bold and to explain why these words are written in this way. • Have students locate these words in the glossary and read the definition for each word.
Lesson 2 **Understanding and using prediction in mental imagery:** Students will be better able to use prediction to help solve math problems.	• Ask students when they might use a prediction strategy (when reading a text). • Ask how prediction can help them when they read a text. • Ask how this strategy can be used to help them solve math problems.
Lesson 3 **Reading a chart:** Students will have a better understanding of how to use a chart to solve a math problem.	• Ask students to identify the headings in the chart. • Ask students to identify the 3-D shapes already listed. • Ask students what section of the chart has not been completed. • Ask how using a chart is a good strategy for solving the problem.
Lesson 4 **Similarities and differences:** Students will understand the differences between a triangle-based prism and a square-based prism.	• Ask students to look at Mandy's drawing of her tent. Ask how closely it resembles the picture of the tent. • Ask students to look at Mandy's drawing of her brother's tent. Ask how it is similar to and different from Mandy's actual tent and her drawing of her tent.
Lesson 5 **Communicating mathematically:** Students will be able to revise the writing and compose a good copy.	• Ask students to review Calvin's rough copy, his comments, and the Communications Checklist. • Ask students what they can do to improve Calvin's rough copy. • Ask students to rewrite Calvin's writing and make changes to improve the writing. • Ask a number of students to read aloud their writing and ask the class to indicate how/whether the revision improves Calvin's rough copy.
Lesson 6 **Understanding the goal statement:** Students will understand the relationship of the goal to the problem.	• Ask students to identify each of the components of the goal statement (estimate the mass of objects; measure the mass of objects; record the mass of objects). • Ask them to read each part of the activity (A to E) and to connect it to part of the goal statement. • Ask if/how the goal is met by completing the activity.
Lesson 7 **Reading the problem closely and carefully:** Students will have a clear understanding of what they are being asked to do.	• Ask students to identify the key words in prompts A to F (extend, list, write). • Ask why identifying the key words will help them complete prompts A to F.
Lesson 8 **Reading a recipe:** Students will have a better understanding of how measurement works in a real-life situation.	• Ask students what kind of information they get from reading the recipe (ingredients, amount of pancakes the recipe makes, size of pancakes, etc.). • Ask students why it is important to read and follow a recipe exactly as written.
Lesson 9 **Communicating mathematically:** Students will apply what they know about communicating mathematically.	• Ask students to explain why it is important to communicate mathematically. • Ask students to read Zola's Model and use the Communication Checklist on p. 303 to determine if Zola has communicated effectively. • Ask if there is anything they would add or change about Zola's Model.
Skills Bank/Problem Bank/Chapter Bank **Finding key information and following directions:** Students will find the information they need to help solve the problems and answer the questions.	• Ask students what they can do to find the key information in the questions in the Skills Bank, the Problem Bank, and the Chapter Review (e.g., read the questions/problems carefully, identify key words, refer to the Communication Checklist on p. 303 when appropriate, etc.).
Chapter Task **Using the task checklist:** Students will have a better understanding of how to complete the task.	• Ask students to explain the purpose of the Task Checklist. • Ask how reviewing the checklist before solving the problem can help them complete the problem.
Cumulative Review/Cross-Strand Multiple Choice **Reading multiple choice questions:** Students will be better prepared to select the correct response to the question.	• Ask students to explain how a multiple choice question is different from other kinds of math questions (many answers provided – need to select correct response). • Ask students what they need to do to ensure they select the correct response (read the question carefully, identify key words, try out different answers).

Chapter Opener

Using the Chapter Opener

Introduce this chapter by discussing the illustration on Student Book page 291, which shows the Cree Village at Moose Factory Island. Students should notice the 3-D shapes within the structure. Ask the class questions such as

* What 2-D and 3-D geometric shapes can you see in the photograph?
* What similar geometric shapes can you see in our classroom?

Draw a 3-column chart on the overhead projector or on a piece of chart paper using the headings "object," "2-D," and "3-D" to record student observations and ideas. Students might say "The windows are rectangles (rectangular)" or "The globe is a ball (sphere)" or "A book is shaped like a box (rectangle-based prism) and I can count 6 rectangles that go together to make the box."

Have a brief discussion about the geometry goals of the chapter, which are listed on page 291. Tell students that the class chart they generated shows examples of *attributes* that can be used to describe 2-D and 3-D shapes. Other attributes to describe these shapes include the number of *vertices* and *edges*, as well as describing the shape and number of the 2-D faces that make up the 3-D shapes.

Ask students to discuss and then record in their journals their thoughts about the measurement goal, using a prompt such as:

* We can measure the *capacity* and *mass* of 3-D shapes. What is meant by *capacity* and *mass*?
* Have you ever used these words before? If so, where?

At the end of the chapter, you can ask students to complete the same prompt and compare their responses and reflect on what they have learned.

At this point, it would be appropriate to:

* send home the Family Newsletter for this chapter
* set up a math bulletin board and math centre for the chapter, displaying a collection of learning materials for this chapter (e.g., sets of 3-D shapes, books on architecture, triangle dot paper, square dot paper, linking cubes, balance scales and masses, and the Problems of the Week)
* assign one of the Problem of the Week problems found in Chapter 11 Teacher's Resource page 3
* ask students to look through the chapter and add math word cards to your classroom word wall. Here are some terms related to this chapter:

congruent	pyramid	2-D	millilitres
kilograms	cylinder	litres	triangle-based
vertex	edges	mass	skeleton model
attributes	capacity	3-D	rectangle-based
faces	volume	prism	tetrahedron
grams	vertices	cone	square-based

3-D Geometry and 3-D Measurement

CHAPTER 11

Goals

You will be able to

* draw, build, and describe 3-dimensional (3-D) shapes
* describe attributes of 3-D shapes
* estimate, measure, and compare the volume, capacity, and mass of 3-D shapes
* make connections between 2-D and 3-D geometry and between geometry and measurement

Cree Village at Moose Factory Island

Family Newsletter Master p. 62

Getting Started: Describing Packages

Grade 3 Skills/Concepts

- Recognize basic 2-D and 3-D shapes.
- Estimate, measure, and record the capacity of containers and the mass of objects.
- Compare the measures using the appropriate terms: millilitre, litre, gram, kilogram.

Use these pages as an opportunity for initial assessment, to give you a sense of students' understanding of and experience with collecting, organizing, recording, and reporting data from Grade 3. Observe what students can do and what they are having difficulty with. Record your notes using the Initial Assessment Summary for each individual.

Preparation and Planning

Pacing	**25–30 min** Activity **10 min** Do You Remember?
Materials	• variety of packages of different sizes, shapes, and masses (2 packages/student) • (optional) ruler, measuring tape, balance scales, and masses
Masters	• 1 cm Grid Paper, Masters Booklet, p. 23 • (for Extra Support) Scaffolding p. 69 • (for Assessment) Initial Assessment Summary, Masters Booklet, p. 1
Vocabulary/ Symbols	pyramid, prism, mass, gram, kilogram, capacity, millilitre, litre, centimetre, congruent

CHAPTER 11

Getting Started

Describing Packages

These students are describing and comparing packages of different sizes and shapes.

? How can you describe the sizes and shapes of the packages?

A. Examine 2 packages in the picture. Make a list of math words that describe each package.

292

Using the Activity (Pairs/Small Groups) ♦ 25–30 min

Have students examine the picture on page 292. In small groups, ask them to discuss what they see the students doing. Review the word list in the illustration. Tell the students that they will be working with similar packages and will need to examine and describe them as thoroughly as possible.

Provide each pair or small group of students with 2 wrapped packages to explore. Ask them to take turns describing the packages to the other students in the group. Encourage students to use the word list. Make the optional tools available to students (e.g., ruler, balance scales) and ask "How can each of these tools be used to gather information that will help you describe your package?" (You can use the ruler to measure the package; you can use the balance scales to weigh the package; you can use the centimetre grid to find the area of one of the sides of the package.) Draw attention to the central question and have students work in pairs or small groups answer prompts A to D.

Listen to how individual students describe the packages. Read their lists. Are their descriptions accurate and complete? If Extra Support is required, guide those students and provide copies of **Scaffolding Master p. 69**.

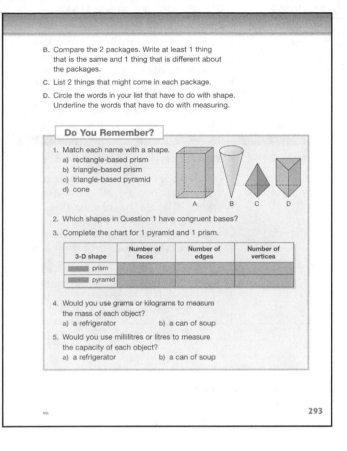

B. Compare the 2 packages. Write at least 1 thing that is the same and 1 thing that is different about the packages.

C. List 2 things that might come in each package.

D. Circle the words in your list that have to do with shape. Underline the words that have to do with measuring.

Do You Remember?

1. Match each name with a shape.
   a) rectangle-based prism
   b) triangle-based prism
   c) triangle-based pyramid
   d) cone

2. Which shapes in Question 1 have congruent bases?

3. Complete the chart for 1 pyramid and 1 prism.

3-D shape	Number of faces	Number of edges	Number of vertices
▬▬ prism			
▬▬ pyramid			

4. Would you use grams or kilograms to measure the mass of each object?
   a) a refrigerator
   b) a can of soup

5. Would you use millilitres or litres to measure the capacity of each object?
   a) a refrigerator
   b) a can of soup

Using Do You Remember?
(Individual) ▶ **10 min**

Observe individual students to see if they can correctly answer the questions. Encourage them to use the 3-D models in the classroom and the word list in the illustration on page 292. Students can also use the optional tools such as a ruler to give more specific descriptions, but make sure that students can use basic words such as *base* and *face* and can also describe the shape of their package accurately. If Extra Support is required, guide those students and provide a copy of **Scaffolding Master p. 70**.

Answers

A. For example,
   a square-based pyramid: square base, 5 faces (1 square and 4 congruent triangles), 5 vertices, 8 edges, holds 250 mL, mass about 20 g;
   a triangle-based prism: triangle base, 5 faces, 2 triangles and 3 rectangles, 6 vertices, 9 edges, congruent rectangle faces and congruent triangle faces, holds 500 mL, mass about 1 kg.

B. For example,
   same: number of faces, both have congruent triangle faces; different: different base shapes, different number of edges and vertices

C. For example,
   pyramid: gift, candle, toy, chocolate
   prism: chocolate, puzzle, tissues

D. For example,
   shape: square, rectangle, triangle, number of faces, edges and vertices
   measuring: holds 250 mL, about 20 g, heavy, light, 30 cm, 12 cm^2

1. a) A
   b) D
   c) C
   d) B

2. A and D

3. For example,

3-D shape	Number of faces	Number of edges	Number of vertices
rectangle-based prism	6	12	8
triangle-based pyramid	4	6	4
triangle-based prism	5	9	6

4. a) kilogram
   b) gram

5. a) litre
   b) millilitre

Describing Packages	When Students Have an Area of Strength	When Students Have an Area of Need
• Parts A–D	• Students will use correct geometry and measurement terms to describe the packages thoroughly.	• Students will have difficulty describing and comparing the packages. Select one package for these students to examine together and focus their attention on the math words on page 292 of the Student Book. Weigh, measure, and record one package together. Students should then record the results individually on the scaffolding master and try to complete a second example with a partner.

Do You Remember?	When Students Have an Area of Strength	When Students Have an Area of Need
• Questions 1–3 (Understanding of Concepts)	• Students will successfully name and describe shapes, including the number of faces, edges, and vertices.	• Students may have difficulty naming the attributes of packages. Select one package and review the number of faces, edges, and vertices. Review the meaning of *congruent*. Help students fill out one row in the chart and then have them complete the other row by themselves.
• Questions 4–5 (Understanding of Concepts)	• Students will successfully identify which unit is used to measure each item.	• Students will be unsure of which unit of measure to use. Determine the mass (or the capacity) of several objects so that students become familiar with each unit of measure.

Extra Support:
Scaffolding Master, p. 69

Assessment: Initial Assessment
Summary, Masters Booklet p. 1

Extra Support:
Scaffolding Master,
p. 70

1 cm Grid Paper,
Masters Booklet p. 23

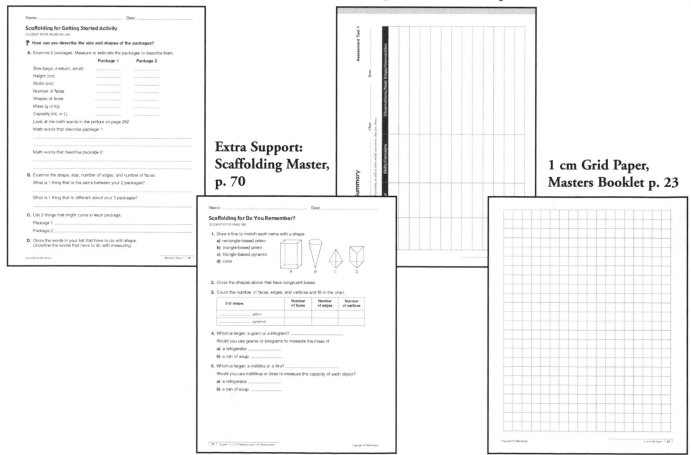

Sketching Faces

Goal Describe relationships between 3-D shapes and their 2-D faces.

Prerequisite Skills/Concepts
- Recognize basic 2-D and 3-D shapes.
- Recognize and count faces and edges of 3-D shapes.

Expectations
4m62 investigate the attributes of three-dimensional figures and two-dimensional shapes using concrete materials and drawings

4m68 investigate the two-dimensional shapes of the faces of three-dimensional figures

4m69 sketch the faces that make up a three-dimensional figure using concrete materials as models

4m80 discuss ideas, make connections, and articulate hypotheses about geometric properties and relationships

Assessment for Feedback	What You Will See Students Doing...	
Students will	**When Students Understand**	**If Students Misunderstand**
• identify the types of prisms and pyramids used	• Students will correctly identify prisms and pyramids by the shapes of their bases.	• Students will not identify the shapes correctly. Provide examples of various prisms and pyramids with the bases labelled. For example, base: square, type: square-based pyramid.
• count edges and faces of prisms and pyramids	• Students will count the number of edges, faces, and sides of faces without difficulty.	• Students may lose count. Provide easily removed stickers to help them keep track of the faces or edges they have counted.

Preparation and Planning

Pacing	**5–10 min** Introduction **25–35 min** Teaching and Learning **10–15 min** Consolidation
Materials	• variety of prisms and pyramids (minimum 1/student)
Masters	• Mental Math p. 63 • 3-D Shapes and 2-D Faces, Master p. 72
Workbook	p. 94
Vocabulary/ Symbols	face, edge, side, prism, pyramid, cube, square-based prism, triangle-based prism, rectangle-based prism, square-based pyramid, triangle-based pyramid, hexagon-based pyramid, and any other 3-D shapes you are using such as cylinder, cone, and sphere
Key Assessment of Learning Question	Entire exploration, Problem Solving

Meeting Individual Needs

Extra Challenge
- Students could be encouraged to select a solid geometric shape and find other objects (inside or outside the classroom) that have a similar 3-D shape. They could also search for objects that have a shape similar to one of the faces of their geometric shape. Have students make a list of the objects they found with similar shapes and note whether the items are manufactured or natural.

Extra Support
- Provide students with a variety of 2-D and 3-D shapes, and have them match the face to the shape (for example, a square and a cube).

1. Introduction (Pairs)
▶ 5–10 min

Distribute a prism and a pyramid to each pair of students and have them discuss how the two shapes are different and how they are the same (e.g., material, colour, number of vertices, edges and faces, shape of faces). To compare their shapes, students will need to use information they already have about the attributes of these shapes.

Sample Discourse

"Is this a prism or a pyramid?"
• *A prism*

"How do you know?"
• *It has two bases, it doesn't come to a point.*

"What shape are the bases?"
• *Triangles*

"What specific type of prism is it?"
• *A triangle-based prism.*

"The base faces are triangles. What shape are the other faces?"
• *Rectangles*

"How many rectangular faces are there?"
• *3*

"How many faces are there all together?"
• *5*

"What do you call the place where the sides of faces meet?"
• *The edges*

"How many edges does this shape have?"
• *9*

Tell students that they will investigate the relationship between 3-D shapes and the 2-D faces.

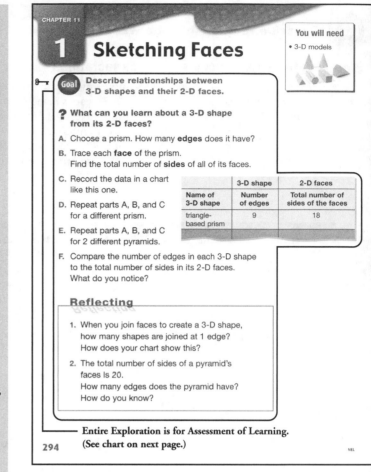

2. Teaching and Learning (Pairs) ▶ 25–35 min

Instruct students to work in pairs with the two shapes you distributed in the introduction. Students can exchange shapes with other students as necessary during the lesson.

Draw attention to the central question and have each pair answer this question by working through prompts A to F. Give each student a copy of the 3-D Shapes and 2-D Faces Master and explain that they should complete their own charts based on the work with their partners. Since this is the first of several Explorations in this chapter where student will work in pairs or small groups, discuss the prompts and have students suggest ways that they could share the various tasks, such as counting edges and faces, verifying the counting, and tracing the faces. Students should examine 2 prisms and 2 pyramids.

Before assigning the Reflecting questions, discuss the results in the chart and the answer to prompt F. Here students relate their work using the blackline master to examine the relationships between 3-D shapes and their 2-D faces.

Reflecting

Use these questions to ensure that students understand the relationship between the number of edges and the total number of sides of the faces in 3-D shapes. Discuss the questions and encourage a variety of responses and examples.

Sample Discourse

1. • *Two shapes are joined at one edge.*
   • *There are half as many edges for each shape as there are sides. For example, a triangle-based prism has 9 edges and 18 sides. The chart shows this because the number in the third column (total number of sides of the faces) is always twice the number in the second column (number of edges).*

2. • *10 edges, because the number of faces is twice (or double) the number of edges. Half of 20 is 10; 20 is double 10.*

Related Question to Ask

Ask	Possible Response
About **Question 2:** • What type of pyramid would have 10 edges?	• *If a pyramid has 10 edges, 5 would be around the base and 5 on the sides. This is a pyramid with a 5-sided base.*

Answers

A.–E. For example:

Name of 3-D shape	3-D shape Number of edges	2-D faces Total number of sides of the faces
triangle-based prism	9	18
cube	12	24
triangle based pyramid	6	12
hexagon-based pyramid	12	24

F. There are half as many edges for each shape as there are sides.

1. 2; the number in the third column is 2 times the number in the second colum.

2. 10 edges; it is half as many as the number of sides.

3. Consolidation ♦ 10–15 min

For intervention strategies, refer to the Meeting Individual Needs box and the Assessment for Feedback chart.

Closing (Whole Class)

Have students summarize their learning by writing a response to the central question.
- *I learned that if you count all the sides of all the faces in a 3-D shape, you know how many edges the 3-D shape has because there are half as many.*

Assessment of Learning—What to Look for in Student Work...

Assessment Strategy: investigation
Problem Solving

Assessment Opportunity
In this exploration lesson, the entire investigation is an opportunity for assessment. You will see students carrying out an inquiry and will be able to observe their ability to use 3-D models to find a relationship between the number of edges in a 3-D shape and the total number of sides in its 2-D faces.

To gather evidence about a student's ability to problem solve, use informal observation, questioning, and written work. Use the Problem Solving Rubric (Tool 6) to help you focus on the problem-solving process. You may want to focus on the "Carry Out the Plan," "Look Back," and "Communicate" rows in the rubric.

Extra Practice and Extension

- You might assign any of the questions related to this lesson, which are cross-referenced in the chart below.

Mid-Chapter Review	Student Book p. 304, Question 1 & 2
Skills Bank	Student Book p. 312, Question 1
Problem Bank	Student Book p. 314, Question 1
Chapter Review	Student Book p. 316, Questions 1 & 2
Workbook	p. 94, all questions
Nelson Web Site	Visit **www.mathk8.nelson.com** and follow the links to *Nelson Mathematics 4*, Chapter 11.

At Home

- Students can find a box and show family members how many faces and edges it has. They can name and sketch anything in their homes that is made by combining 3-D shapes.

Math Background

When faces are joined to create a 3-D shape, two separate edges become one; students will notice that, as a result, the number of edges of a 3-D shape is always half of the number of total edges for the separated faces, whether for prisms or pyramids.

Some students might also observe that the number of edges of a prism is always three times the number of edges of the base and that the number of edges of a pyramid is always two times the number of edges on the base. This is because, for a prism, the number of edges on each base is the same and is determined by the number of sides of the base; as well, the same number of edges connect the two bases because there is one edge at each vertex of a base and there are the same number of vertices as edges. For a pyramid, there is only one base and one set of edges connecting the base to the top vertex, so the number of edges on the base is only doubled, not tripled.

In this exploration of 3-D shapes, students need to be encouraged to describe what they see using geometric and measurement terms at point of use. Teachers should recognize that students will also use "non-mathematical" terms to describe the shapes. This does not indicate a lack of understanding. For example, they might say "kite" or "diamond" for a rhombus or a parallelogram when describing faces of prisms or pyramids. Students will probably also use the term *box* for rectangular prism or cube. These are not incorrect, but there are more sophisticated and precise mathematical terms that students will learn over the course of the chapter. See the Preparation and Planning Chart for specific vocabulary.

Curious Math: Faces, Edges, and Vertices

Using Curious Math

Materials: 2 prisms, 2 pyramids, calculators (optional)
Masters: 3-D Shapes and 2-D Faces p. 72

There are interesting numerical relationships inherent in geometric shapes. When students collect information about shapes in an organized way (e.g., by using a table) they find the patterns that will help them make predictions about other shapes. Have students work in pairs to complete the table and find the number patterns among the faces, vertices, and edges of 3-D shapes. Ask students to share their answers for questions 1 a) and b).

Answers

1. a) **Pyramids:** If you know the shape of a pyramid's base, multiply the number of sides of the base by 2 to determine the number of edges. For example, for a triangle-based pyramid, there are 3 sides in the base. Multiply $3 \times 2 = 6$. There are 6 edges. For a pentagon-based pyramid, there are 5 sides in the base. Multiply $5 \times 2 = 10$. There are 10 edges.

   b) **Prisms:** If you know the shape of a prism's base, multiply the number of sides of the base by 3 to determine the number of edges. For example, for a triangle-based prism, there are 3 sides in the base. Multiply $3 \times 3 = 9$. There are 9 edges. For a rectangle-based prism, there are 4 sides in the base. Multiply $4 \times 3 = 12$. There are 12 edges.

2.

3-D shape	Number of faces	Number of vertices	Number of edges
triangle-based prism	5	6	9
hexagon-based prism	8	12	18
triangle-based pyramid	4	4	6
hexagon-based pyramid	7	7	12

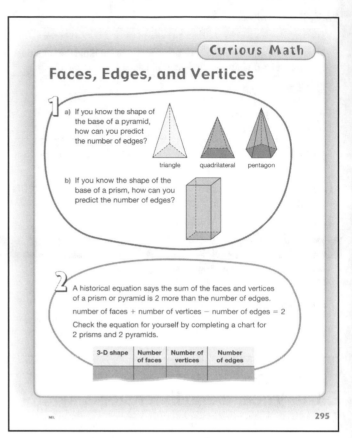

Curious Math

Faces, Edges, and Vertices

1. a) If you know the shape of the base of a pyramid, how can you predict the number of edges?

   triangle   quadrilateral   pentagon

   b) If you know the shape of the base of a prism, how can you predict the number of edges?

2. A historical equation says the sum of the faces and vertices of a prism or pyramid is 2 more than the number of edges.

   number of faces + number of vertices − number of edges = 2

   Check the equation for yourself by completing a chart for 2 prisms and 2 pyramids.

3-D shape	Number of faces	Number of vertices	Number of edges

295

Building 3-D Shapes with Congruent Faces

Goal Build 3-D shapes and describe relationships between faces and vertices.

Prerequisite Skills/Concepts
- Identify the characteristics of 2-D shapes (squares and triangles).
- Use nets to construct 3-D shapes.

Expectations
4m62 investigate the attributes of three-dimensional figures and two-dimensional shapes using concrete materials and drawings

4m63 draw and build three-dimensional objects and models

4m67 use language effectively to describe geometric concepts, reasoning, and investigations[, and coordinate systems]

4m68 identify the two-dimensional shapes of the faces of three-dimensional figures

Assessment for Feedback	What You Will See Students Doing...	
Students will	**When Students Understand**	**If Students Misunderstand**
• identify the attributes of 2-D shapes (face, vertex/vertices, and side) by connecting the names to the parts of squares and triangles	• Students will answer with the correct word when you point to one of the attributes on a 3-D shape model.	• Students who use the incorrect words for particular attributes will benefit from a simple classroom chart that shows a 3-D shape with its attributes clearly labelled.
• use nets to construct 3-D shapes	• Students will join congruent equilateral triangles into nets, and fold these nets into 3-D shapes.	• If students have difficulty making nets and 3-D shapes, have them make an "open" pyramid by omitting the base and using 3 or 4 triangles. Remind students that they are making closed shapes, with all faces made with a paper triangle.
• describe relationships between the faces and vertices of 3-D shapes	• Students will record the faces, vertices, and edges of their 3-D shapes in a table.	• Some students may not have experience filling in this type of table. Support them by working through their first shape and showing them where to write their answers on the table.

Preparation and Planning

Pacing	**5–10 min** Introduction **30–40 min** Teaching and Learning **5–10 min** Consolidation
Materials	• 3-D shapes, such as cubes, prisms, or pyramids • 1 pair scissors/small group of students • 30 construction paper equilateral triangles/group • 16 construction paper squares/group • 1 roll of tape/group
Masters	• Mental Math p. 63 • 1 cm Square Dot Paper, Masters Booklet p. 25 • Triangle Dot Paper, Masters Booklet p. 26 • 3-D Shapes Chart p. 73
Workbook	p. 95
Vocabulary/ Symbols	net, face, vertex, vertices, congruent, pyramid (triangle-based and square-based), prism (triangle-based or rectangle-based), cube
Key Assessment of Learning Question	Entire exploration, Problem Solving

Meeting Individual Needs

Extra Challenge
- Students could construct 3-D shapes using squares and triangles. Have them write about the number of faces that meet at each vertex in these shapes.

Extra Support
- Some students may not work quickly enough to build with triangles and squares. Reducing the number of objects (e.g., build shapes with 4, 5, and 6 faces, rather than "2 faces through to 10" as described in Part A) would allow these children to construct and describe the relationship between vertices and faces.

1. Introduction (Whole Class)
▶ 5–10 min

Display a model of a 3-D shape. Point to faces, vertices, and edges, and ask students to name and count these attributes. Ask students how many faces come together at each vertex. Tell students they are going to make their own 3-D shapes using equilateral triangles and squares.

2. Teaching and Learning (Small Groups/Whole Class) ▶ 30–40 min

Draw attention to the picture of the geodesic dome on Student Book page 296 and ask if any students have seen the dome or any other structures similar to the one pictured. Point out that the geodesic dome is made of congruent triangles.

Distribute the triangles, squares, tape, and a copy of 3-D Shapes Chart to each group. Direct attention to the central question. Tell students they are going to answer this question by constructing at least 2 shapes from the triangles, and 1 shape from the squares. You might want to assign 2 shapes from the 3-D Shapes Chart to each group, to ensure that all of the shapes listed in the chart will be made in the class. Make it clear to the students that some of the shapes may not be possible to make.

Have students answer the central question by answering the parts. Demonstrate taping two triangles. Instruct students to complete their own charts using their group's findings. Before assigning the Reflecting questions, bring the groups together to discuss the answers to Parts A to C and have groups fill in any missing information on their charts.

Reflecting

Use these questions to ensure that students understand the relationship between faces and vertices. Discuss the questions and encourage varied responses.

Sample Discourse

1. • *We built more with triangles because the numbers of vertices of the triangle is smaller than the number of vertices of the squares, so it is possible to get different numbers of faces meeting at the triangle vertices.*
   • *We made a lot more with triangles because the square would only make a cube, with 6 faces. I think it has to do with the angles at the vertices.*
2. • *With shapes made from triangles, the number of faces was the same as or greater than the number of vertices. But with the shape made from squares, the number of faces was less than the number of vertices.*
   • *Most of the shapes made with triangles had more faces than vertices, except for the shape made with 4 triangles, which had 4 faces and 4 vertices. The square had only 6 faces, but 8 vertices.*
3. • *The fewest number of faces that met at a vertex was 3. This was in the shape made with 4 triangles. Some shapes had the same number at each vertex; others had different numbers.*

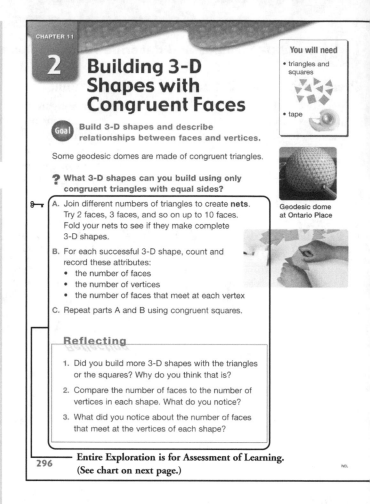

2 Building 3-D Shapes with Congruent Faces

Goal Build 3-D shapes and describe relationships between faces and vertices.

Some geodesic domes are made of congruent triangles.

? What 3-D shapes can you build using only congruent triangles with equal sides?

A. Join different numbers of triangles to create **nets**. Try 2 faces, 3 faces, and so on up to 10 faces. Fold your nets to see if they make complete 3-D shapes.

B. For each successful 3-D shape, count and record these attributes:
   • the number of faces
   • the number of vertices
   • the number of faces that meet at each vertex

C. Repeat parts A and B using congruent squares.

You will need
• triangles and squares
• tape

Geodesic dome at Ontario Place

Reflecting

1. Did you build more 3-D shapes with the triangles or the squares? Why do you think that is?
2. Compare the number of faces to the number of vertices in each shape. What do you notice?
3. What did you notice about the number of faces that meet at the vertices of each shape?

Entire Exploration is for Assessment of Learning.
(See chart on next page.)

296   NEL

• *The shapes that looked the same no matter how you held them, such as the pyramid made with 4 triangles, had the same number of faces at each vertex. The other ones had different numbers of faces at the vertices.*

Answers

A.–C. 3-D Shapes Chart

Number of triangles/squares	Number of faces	Number of vertices	Number of faces at each vertex
1–3 triangles	not possible		
4 triangles	4	4	3 faces at each
5 triangles	not possible		
6 triangles	6	5	3 faces meet at 2 vertices 4 faces meet at 3 vertices
7 triangles	not possible		
8 triangles	8	6	4 faces meet at each
9 triangles	not possible		
10 triangles	10	7	5 faces meet at the 2 "top" vertices 4 faces meet at 5 "base" vertices
1–5 squares	not possible		
6 squares	6	8	3 faces meet at each
7–10 squares	not possible		

1. **Triangles.** With triangles, you can have 3, 4, or 5 faces meeting at a point, but with squares only 3 faces can meet so there are fewer possibilities.

2. Usually there are more faces than vertices except for a cube and a triangle-based pyramid.

3. For some shapes, the same number of faces meet at each vertex (e.g., for a tetrahedron made of 4 triangles, 3 faces meet at each of the 4 vertices). For other shapes, different numbers meet at its vertices.

3. **Consolidation** ▸ 5–10 min

Checking (Small Groups)

For intervention strategies, refer to the Meeting Individual Needs box and the Assessment for Feedback chart.

Closing (Whole Class)

Have students summarize what they have learned by asking "What have you learned about the relationships between faces and vertices of 3-D shapes that are made from congruent faces?" They might write their responses in their math journals.

- *The relationships between faces and vertices vary for the triangle shapes. The shape made with 4 triangles also has 4 faces. The other triangle shapes have more faces than vertices. The cube has more vertices than faces.*

Assessment of Learning—What to Look for in Student Work...

Assessment Strategy: investigation
Problem Solving

Assessment Opportunity
In this exploration lesson, the entire investigation is an opportunity for assessment. You will see students carrying out an inquiry and will be able to observe their ability to use triangles and squares to create nets to find a relationship between the faces and vertices.

To gather evidence about a student's ability to problem solve, use informal observation, questioning, and written work. Use the Problem Solving Rubric (Tool 6) to help you focus on the problem solving process. You may want to focus on the "Carry Out the Plan," "Look Back," and "Communicate" rows in the rubric.

Extra Practice and Extension

- You might assign any of the questions related to this lesson, which are cross-referenced in the chart below.

Skills Bank	Student Book p. 312, Question 2
Problem Bank	Student Book p. 314, Question 2
Workbook	p. 95, all questions
Nelson Web Site	Visit **www.mathk8.nelson.com** and follow the links to *Nelson Mathematics 4*, Chapter 11.

At Home

- Students could make a list of objects in their homes that are similar to the 3-D shapes they constructed in this lesson. Have them describe the object, explain how it is used, and then describe the material it is made from. For example, storage boxes are cubes; candy boxes might be shaped like prisms or pyramids.

Math Background

It is not necessary for students to learn the names of these shapes, although mathematicians call the entire group of shapes made from equilateral triangles "deltahedra." The key idea is for students to know that some of the shapes have the same number of faces joining at each vertex (regular shapes have congruent edge lengths and congruent angles), while others will have different numbers of faces meeting at each vertex (irregular).

3-D shapes made from congruent equilateral triangles can have only 3, 4, or 5 faces meeting at each vertex, because the angle at each vertex of the triangle faces is 60°. If the vertices of 6 equilateral triangles meet, 6 × 60° forms a 360° angle, which is flat; 2 triangles are not enough to form a 3-D shape.

There are only 5 regular polyhedra (congruent faces and angles; same number faces/edges meet at each vertex), and only 3 are also deltahedra: the tetrahedron, octahedron, and icosahedron.

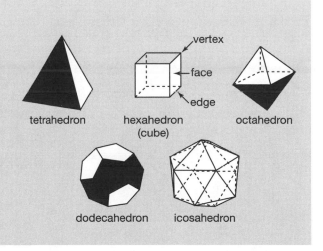

tetrahedron   hexahedron   octahedron
(cube)

dodecahedron   icosahedron

Mental Imagery: Cross-Sections

Using the Mental Imagery

Materials: modelling clay and dental floss for each small group

Masters: none

This page provides the opportunity for students to predict, and then determine physically, the 2-D and 3-D shapes created by cutting across prisms and pyramids. Developing the ability to visualize the new shapes created by cutting across the original prisms and pyramids helps consolidate students' understanding of the relationships between the 3-D shapes and their 2-D faces.

Answers

A. New faces are squares and new 3-D shapes are rectangular prisms.

B. New faces are squares and new 3-D shapes are rectangular prisms.

C. New faces are rectangles; the larger 3-D shape is irregular (6 faces, 10 vertices, 15 edges); the smaller shape is a triangle-based pyramid.

1. The "new" faces are triangles, congruent to the triangular faces on the original 3-D shape.

2. The 2 new faces are both pentagons; the top portion is still a pentagon-based pyramid, and the bottom section is an irregular pentagon-based prism.

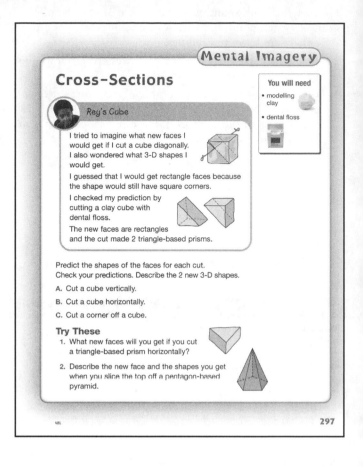

Mental Imagery

Cross-Sections

You will need
- modelling clay
- dental floss

Rey's Cube

I tried to imagine what new faces I would get if I cut a cube diagonally. I also wondered what 3-D shapes I would get.

I guessed that I would get rectangle faces because the shape would still have square corners.

I checked my prediction by cutting a clay cube with dental floss.

The new faces are rectangles and the cut made 2 triangle-based prisms.

Predict the shapes of the faces for each cut. Check your predictions. Describe the 2 new 3-D shapes.

A. Cut a cube vertically.

B. Cut a cube horizontally.

C. Cut a corner off a cube.

Try These
1. What new faces will you get if you cut a triangle-based prism horizontally?

2. Describe the new face and the shapes you get when you slice the top off a pentagon-based pyramid.

297

Goal Build 3-D skeletons and describe relationships between edges and vertices.

Prerequisite Skills/Concepts

- Describe the attributes of 3-D figures and 2-D shapes.
- Use language effectively to describe geometric concepts, reasoning, and investigations.

Expectations

4m62 investigate the attributes of three-dimensional figures [and two-dimensional shapes] using concrete materials [and drawings]

4m63 [draw and] build three-dimensional objects and models

4m70 design and make skeletons for three-dimensional figures

4m79 discuss geometric concepts with peers and explain their understanding of the concepts

4m80 discuss ideas, make connections, and articulate hypotheses about geometric properties and relationships

Assessment for Feedback	What You Will See Students Doing...	
Students will	**When Students Understand**	**If Students Misunderstand**
• design and make skeletons given certain attributes (e.g., the number of vertices in the shape)	• Students will build a variety of skeleton models using a given number of vertices.	• Some students may find it challenging to begin the exploration with a given number of vertices. Have these students build any skeleton shape then record their findings. Ask students which skeletons can be built with a given number of vertices.
• discuss geometric concepts with peers and explain their understanding of the concepts	• Students will use the chart they create to see patterns in the relationship between vertices and edges in their skeleton shapes.	• Students who have difficulty noticing patterns and communicating their findings in writing may benefit from sentence prompts that get them started describing the pertinent relationships.
• disuss ideas, make connections, and articulate hypotheses about geometric relationships	• Students will clearly describe the relationships between vertices and edges that they notice in the chart.	• Students experiencing difficulty phrasing their responses could be paired with other students who could assist them.

Preparation and Planning

Pacing	**5–10 min** Introduction **25–35 min** Teaching and Learning **5–10 min** Consolidation
Materials	• toothpicks (50/pair) • modelling clay • (for Extra Challenge) 50 bamboo skewers
Masters	• Mental Math p. 63
Workbook	p. 96
Vocabulary/ Symbols	edge, vertex, vertices
Key Assessment of Learning Question	Entire exploration, Problem Solving

Meeting Individual Needs

Extra Challenge

- Students could be challenged to choose their favourite shape and make a large model using bamboo skewers.
- Students could explore stellated (star-shaped) solids. First, students build a skeleton model of a cube. Next, they use each square face of the cube as the base of a square-based pyramid. Use 4 edges and one more vertex to build a pyramid on each face to create a star-like shape.
- Students could make a skeleton dome using the following directions: (1) Form a base by connecting 5 toothpicks and 5 pieces of modelling clay in a ring. (2) From each ball of modelling clay in the base ring, make a triangle using 2 toothpicks and 1 more piece of modelling clay. (3) Repeat step 2 all the way around the base until there are 5 triangles. (4) Connect the pieces of modelling clay at the top of the triangles with toothpicks. There should be 10 triangles. (5) Insert a toothpick into each piece of modelling clay along the top ring and use one piece of modelling clay to connect them all.

Extra Support

- Pair students with a good understanding of the activity and good communication skills with students who need extra support.

1. Introduction (Whole Class)
▶ 5–10 min

Before students open their books, show them large skeleton models of the same triangle-based prism and pentagon-based prism as on page 298 of the Student Book that you have made from modelling clay and bamboo skewers. Discuss what is the same and what is different about the two shapes. Encourage students to compare the vertices and edges of the two structures. The structures have the same number of vertices but a different number of edges. Tell students they are going to make skeleton models.

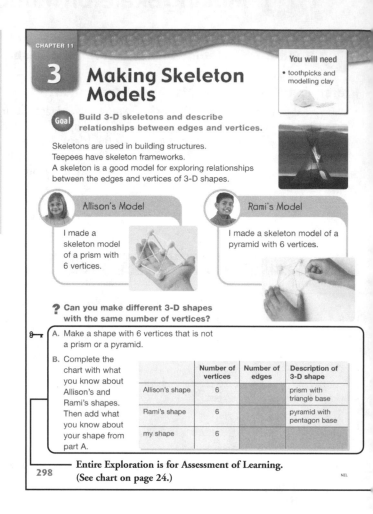

2. Teaching and Learning (Pairs) ▶ 25–35 min

Have students look at the photograph of the tepee on Student Book page 298 and ask how a skeleton is used to make this structure. (The poles create a skeleton for the structure.) Ask students to identify the edges and vertices in the tepee. Repeat with Allison's and Rami's model.

Read the central question. Distribute materials to each pair of students. Read prompt A and discuss how to record results in the chart. Students work with toothpicks to make 3-D shapes with congruent edges. Students need to make only 2 pairs of 3-D shapes, each with the same number of vertices, to discover that:

• different shapes with the same number of vertices have different numbers of edges

• there are always more edges than vertices in a shape

Students could mark each edge with a marker or removable stickers as they count it so that they don't lose count. Students can double-check their partner's work.

Reflecting

Use these questions to ensure that students are comparing the number of edges and vertices in different shapes. Discuss the questions and encourage varied responses.

Sample Discourse

1. • *There are always more edges than vertices in 3-D shapes.*
   • *Every vertex holds more than one edge.*
2. • *I could only build one shape with 4 vertices.*
   • *I could only build a triangle-based pyramid.*
3. • *If you have an odd number of vertices, you can predict the shape will be a pyramid. If you have an even number of vertices, the shape could be a prism or a pyramid.*

C. Make 2 or more different 3-D shapes, each with the same number of vertices.
Add the new information to your chart from part B.

Reflecting

1. Compare the number of edges to the number of vertices for each shape. What do you notice?

2. Is it possible to build a 3-D shape with 4 vertices? Explain your answer.

3. Suppose you know the number of vertices of a shape. Can you predict what the shape will look like? Explain your thinking.

Curious Math

Making Shadows

A shadow is made when light shines through a skeleton. What shapes could the skeletons that made these shadows be? Explain your answers.

1. a)   b)   c)

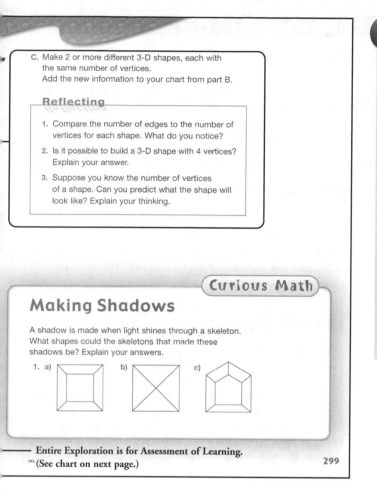

Entire Exploration is for Assessment of Learning.
NEL (See chart on next page.)

299

---

3. Consolidation ♦ 5–10 min

For intervention strategies, refer to the Meeting Individual Needs box and the Assessment for Feedback chart.

Closing (Whole Class)

Have students summarize what they have learned by asking, "Were you surprised by the fact that different skeletons could have the same number of vertices?" Lead students to explore and explain the numerical patterns revealed as they completed the chart.

"Which number of vertices make the most different skeleton models?"

• *6 vertices (triangle-based prism, pentagon-based pyramid); 8 vertices (cube, rectangle-based prism) and 12 vertices because they can be prisms or pyramids.*

"Which number of vertices make the fewest different skeletons?"

• *Odd numbered vertices*
• *6 vertices or less*

Answers

A. – B.

	Number of vertices	Number of edges	Description of 3-D Shape
Allison's shape	6	9	prism with triangle base
Rami's shape	6	10	pyramid with pentagon base
my shape	6	12	shape with 8 triangle faces

Three possible shapes made with 6 vertices.

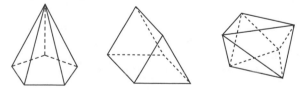

C. For example:

	Number of vertices	Number of edges	Description of 3-D shape
Shape 1	5	8	pyramid with square base
Shape 2	5	9	2 triangle-based pyramids attached
Shape 3	9	16	pyramid with octagon base
Shape 4	9	16	cube with a square-based pyramid on top

1. For example, there are always more edges than vertices in a shape. If 2 different shapes have the same number of vertices, they will have a different number of edges.

2. There is only 1 shape possible for 4 vertices (a tetrahedron, or triangle-based pyramid).

3. For example, no, because different shapes can have the same number of vertices.

For example, you need an even number of vertices to build a prism because you need to build 2 bases and they have to be exactly the same.

For pyramids, you can have an odd or an even number of bases. You keep one for the top of the vertex and then use the rest to make a base shape.

Assessment Strategy: investigation
Problem Solving

Assessment Opportunity
In this exploration lesson, the entire investigation is an opportunity for assessment. You will see students carrying out an inquiry and will be able to observe their ability to use toothpicks and modelling clay to build 3-D skeletons. You will then observe students complete a chart to find a relationship between the number of edges to the number of vertices for 3-D shapes.
   To gather evidence about a student's ability to problem solve, use informal observation, questioning, and written work. Use the Problem Solving Rubric (Tool 6) to help you focus on the problem-solving process. You may want to focus on the "Make a Plan," "Carry Out the Plan," "Look Back," and "Communicate" rows in the rubric.

Extra Practice and Extension

- You might assign any of the questions related to this lesson, which are cross-referenced in the chart below.

Mid-Chapter Review	Student Book p. 304, Question 3
Skills Bank	Student Book p. 312, Question 3
Problem Bank	Student Book p. 314, Questions 3, 4, & 5
Chapter Review	Student Book p. 316, Question 3
Workbook	p. 96, all questions
Nelson Web Site	Visit **www.mathk8.nelson.com** and follow the links to *Nelson Mathematics 4*, Chapter 11.

At Home

- Have students take their skeleton models home and describe the attributes of each shape to their families.
- Students could play a guessing game with their parents or siblings. Find things that are similar and different about pairs of shapes.

Math Background

Students might assume that they will always get the same shape if they work with a certain number of vertices or edges. This activity allows them to challenge this assumption. Some students may recognize that if a pyramid has a certain number of vertices, the number of edges of the base must be one less than that number of vertices. If the shape were a prism, the number would need to be divided in two to determine the number of vertices or edges of the prism's base.

Curious Math: Making Shadows

Using Curious Math

Materials: (optional) skeleton shapes from Lesson 3, flashlight or table lamp

You may want to demonstrate how shining a light through a skeleton shape that you made in Lesson 3 makes a shadow as suggested in this activity. This will help students who have difficulty translating the 2-D shadows on Student Book page 299, to the 3-D skeleton shapes they made. Suggest that students pretend they are looking *down* on the shape.

Answers

1. a) This is a square-based prism (cube) because there are 2 squares (bases) connected with edges.
   b) This is a square-based pyramid because there is a square and 4 triangle faces.
   c) This is a pentagon-based prism because there are 2 pentagons (bases) with corresponding vertices connected with edges.

Math Background

The shadow activity presents familiar 3-D shapes in a 2-D representation, but from a birds-eye view. It also gives students the opportunity to identify the 3-D shapes based on the attributes they can see (shape of the bases, number of edges, and vertices).

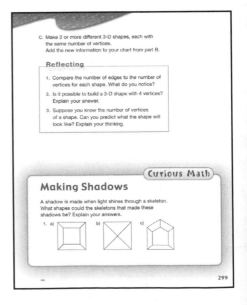

Drawing 3-D Shapes

 Goal **Draw prisms and pyramids.**

Prerequisite Skills/Concepts

- Identify faces, vertices, and edges of 3-D shapes by name.
- Identify and discriminate between a pyramid and a prism.

Expectations

4m63 draw and build three-dimensional objects and models

4m68 identify the two-dimensional faces of three-dimensional figures

Assessment for Feedback	What You Will See Students Doing...	
Students will	**When Students Understand**	**If Students Misunderstand**
• draw a triangle-based prism using the triangle from a set of pattern blocks	• Students will successfully draw a triangle-based prism.	• Students may not successfully complete the drawing. If students make mistakes in joining the vertices of the 2 triangles, suggest they number each vertex in the same way on both triangles. Then, they can join vertex 1 on the first triangle to vertex 1 on the second triangle, and so on.
• draw a square-based pyramid using the square from a set of pattern blocks	• Students will successfully draw a square-based pyramid.	• Students may not successfully complete the drawing. If students place the vertex point too close or too far from the square, suggest they measure a distance of about 4 cm from the top edge of the square.

Preparation and Planning

Pacing	**5–10 min** Introduction **15–20 min** Teaching and Learning **20–30 min** Consolidation
Materials	• 1 pattern block triangle and square/student • ruler/student • 1 circular counter/student • 2 dice/pair of students
Masters	• Mental Math p. 63 • (optional) Triangle Dot Paper, Masters Booklet, p. 26
Workbook	p. 97
Vocabulary/ Symbols	perspective
Key Assessment of Learning Question	Question 6, Application of Procedures

Meeting Individual Needs

Extra Challenge

- Have a variety of 3-D shapes available and challenge students to draw them using triangle dot paper.
- Students could draw in shadows (shading) to enhance the 3-D effect of their drawings. You could use a light source to emphasize the position of the shadows.
- Students could create a collage of 3-D shapes, drawn with perspective, cut and pasted onto a background paper.

Extra Support

- Assist students having difficulty by completing Question 9 as a whole class. Ensure that students understand that they can use the same principles that they used to draw the triangle-based prism and the square-based pyramid to draw a cylinder and a cone.

Introduction (Whole Class)
▶ 5–10 min

Display a variety of 3-D pictures and discuss what illustrators do to make objects appear 3-dimensional on a 2-dimensional page. Tell students they are going to draw 3-D shapes.

Sample Discourse

"Why might it be harder to draw pictures of 3-D shapes than 2-D shapes?"
* *2-D shapes are flat to begin with, but drawings of 3-D shapes have to look like they take up space.*

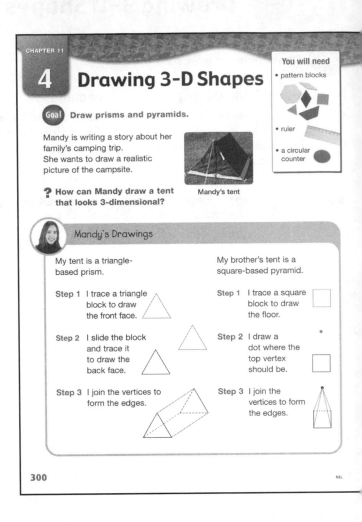

Teaching and Learning (Whole Class) ▶ 15–20 min

Draw attention to the central question and Mandy's Drawings on Student Book page 300. Demonstrate the drawing process for both shapes on an overhead, on the board, or on chart paper. Remind students that while both shapes are made of triangles and rectangles (a square being a rectangle with all sides equal in length), only the pyramid has a vertex on the top. Point out that the base of any 3-D shape is the face that rests on a flat surface, and that the triangles in the prism can be the base if they rest on the supporting surface. Model this idea using a triangle-based prism. Have students follow Mandy's steps to draw their own triangle-based prisms and square-based prism.

Reflecting

Use these questions to ensure that students have developed strategies for creating 3-D perspective. Discuss the questions and encourage a variety of individual responses.

Sample Discourse

1. • *Mandy could erase the dotted lines to show that they are hidden.*
   • *Mandy could draw shadows on the shady side of each tent.*

2. • *When you draw the prism you need to trace around the triangle face twice, then join the vertices. When you draw the pyramid you only draw the base once, then join all the vertices of the square to the point to make the point of the pyramid at the top of the tent.*

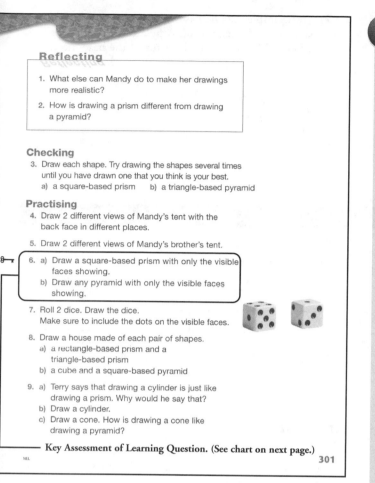

Reflecting

1. What else can Mandy do to make her drawings more realistic?

2. How is drawing a prism different from drawing a pyramid?

Checking

3. Draw each shape. Try drawing the shapes several times until you have drawn one that you think is your best.
   a) a square-based prism   b) a triangle-based pyramid

Practising

4. Draw 2 different views of Mandy's tent with the back face in different places.

5. Draw 2 different views of Mandy's brother's tent.

6. a) Draw a square-based prism with only the visible faces showing.
   b) Draw any pyramid with only the visible faces showing.

7. Roll 2 dice. Draw the dice. Make sure to include the dots on the visible faces.

8. Draw a house made of each pair of shapes.
   a) a rectangle-based prism and a triangle-based prism
   b) a cube and a square-based pyramid

9. a) Terry says that drawing a cylinder is just like drawing a prism. Why would he say that?
   b) Draw a cylinder.
   c) Draw a cone. How is drawing a cone like drawing a pyramid?

— **Key Assessment of Learning Question. (See chart on next page.)**

NEL **301**

3. Consolidation ▶ 20–30 min

Checking (Individual)

For intervention strategies, refer to the Meeting Individual Needs box or the Assessment for Feedback chart.

Remind students that a square-based prism doesn't contain any triangles. A square-based prism can also be called a cube, because it is a type of rectangular prism in which all sides are of equal length. Encourage students to begin the triangle-based pyramid by drawing the triangle base first, and then joining the vanishing point to each of the triangle's 3 vertices.

Practising (Individual)

4.–8. Encourage students to use physical models (e.g., pattern block triangles, squares, and real dice) to draw their 3-D shapes. Refer to the drawings developed in Teaching and Learning, as well as to the illustrations in the book, as they make their drawings.

Closing (Whole Class)

Ask students to summarize what they have learned by asking "How can you draw a tent or a box that looks three-dimensional?" Have students draw either a prism or a pyramid, labelling the faces appropriately.

• *For a prism, first you draw the front face or base. (We did it by tracing a triangle shape. We also drew a square when we sketched the die.) Then you slide the triangle or square up and a bit to the side and draw the back face or base. Next, you join the vertices to form edges. To draw a pyramid, you trace the base and then draw a dot where the vertex is. Then, you join the vertices to form the edges.*

Answers

1. For example, drawings can be made more realistic by erasing hidden edges, adding shadows, and drawing windows and/or a door.

2. For example, for a prism you have to draw the 2 congruent bases and then connect them. For a pyramid, there is only 1 base and you connect its vertices at the top vertex.

3. a)   b)

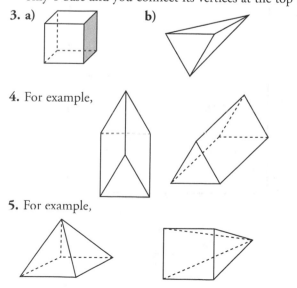

4. For example,

5. For example,

6. a) For example,   b) For example,

7. For example,

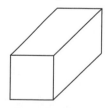

8. a) For example,   b) For example,

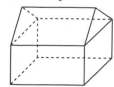

9. a) For example, Terry could say that drawing a cylinder is just like drawing a prism because the two bases of a cylinder are congruent circles. The two bases of any prism are also congruent.

b)

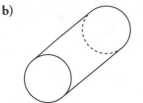

c) For example, a cone has a vertex where all lines starting at the base meet. A pyramid has a vertex where all lines from each vertex of the base meet.

Assessment of Learning—What to Look for in Student Work...

Assessment Strategy: short answer
Application of Procedures

Key Assessment Question 6
a) Draw a square-based prism with only the visible faces showing.
b) Draw any pyramid with only the visible faces showing.

1	2	3	4
• makes major errors and/or omissions when drawing prism and pyramid	• makes several errors and/or omissions when drawing prism and pyramid	• makes only a few minor errors and/or omissions when drawing prism and pyramid	• makes almost no errors when drawing prism and pyramid

Extra Practice and Extension

• You might assign any of the questions related to this lesson, which are cross-referenced in the chart below.

Mid-Chapter Review	Student Book p. 304, Question 4
Skills Bank	Student Book p. 312, Question 4
Chapter Review	Student Book p. 316, Question 4
Workbook	p. 97, all questions
Nelson Web Site	Visit **www.mathk8.nelson.com** and follow the links to *Nelson Mathematics 4*, Chapter 11.

At Home

• Students can look at home for at least one object that is constructed of one or more of the 3-D shapes they learned to draw in this lesson.

**Triangle Dot Paper,
Masters Booklet, p. 26**

Math Background

The two perspective drawing strategies that are developed in this lesson do not exhaust the possibilities, and students may well have developed their own strategies. Encourage these students to share their strategies, and to talk about how they are the same/different as the strategies in the Student Book.

There are a variety of books on architecture available for children, in which strategies for drawing 3-D shapes in the form of buildings are illustrated. Some strategies involve using isometric grid paper.

5 Communicate an Understanding of Geometric Concepts

Goal Use math language to show what you know about a 3-D shape.

Prerequisite Skills/Concepts

- Identify the attributes of triangular prisms and pyramids.
- Construct skeleton models of 3-D shapes.
- Use the writing terms *rough copy* and *good copy*.

Expectations

4m67 use language effectively to describe geometric concepts, reasoning, and investigations [and coordinate systems]

4m77 use mathematical language to describe geometric ideas

4m79 discuss geometric concepts with peers and explain their understanding of the concepts

Assessment for Feedback	What You Will See Students Doing...	
Students will	**When Students Understand**	**If Students Misunderstand**
• use the Communication Checklist to evaluate the sample of math writing	• Students will refer to the Checklist on Student Book page 303, to assess the strengths and weaknesses of their own and others' written descriptions.	• If students have had little previous experience with explaining their math reasoning in writing, scaffold their writing by providing a sample sentence frame: *I think … because …*.
• use toothpicks and modelling clay to construct a triangle-based prism or a cube	• Students will accurately insert the toothpicks into the clay vertices to form the edges of the prism or cube.	• If students are unable to construct a triangle-based prism or a cube, suggest they work in pairs.
• write a description of life in a house shaped like a triangle-based prism or a cube, using math language to describe the physical attributes	• Students will identify the number and position of the faces, edges, vertices, and roof shape for the chosen house.	• If students find it difficult to visualize the faces and edges in the buildings, suggest they make a skeleton model (to show edges) and attach paper to the skeleton (to show faces).
• use the Communication Checklist to edit written description of houses	• Students will make revisions to the written descriptions based on the Communication Checklist using math language (e.g., *vertices* rather than *corners*).	• Some students may have difficulty using math words. Refer them to a chart or list that provides the math terms as well as non-math terms.

Preparation and Planning

Pacing	**5–10 min** Introduction **15–20 min** Teaching and Learning **20–30 min** Consolidation
Materials	• 10 toothpicks/small group of students • 1 ball of modelling clay/small group of students
Masters	• Mental Math Master p. 63 • (for Extra Support) Scaffolding Master p. 71
Workbook	p. 98
Vocabulary/Symbols	tetrahedron
Key Assessment of Learning Question	Question 4, Communication

Meeting Individual Needs

Extra Challenge

- Encourage students to consider all the shapes in the pictures of the buildings. For example, the Eco-Lodge prism is sandwiched between 2 rectangular prisms, which have been sliced on an angle to join the faces of the central prism. The cube house is made of 3 connected, but different-sized cubes. Students could describe the insides of these spaces of the extended buildings, discussing whether or not the original faces of the 3-D shapes are retained inside the structures.
- Students could use pictures from books or Internet sites about architecture and write descriptions using math language.

Extra Support

- Suggest students use their own classroom as a model for observing the inside of a 3-D shape, as required throughout this lesson.

1. Introduction (Whole Class)
▶ 5–10 min

Display a tetrahedron skeleton model, and ask students to describe the attributes of this 3-D shape.

Sample Discourse

"Describe this 3-D shape using math language such as faces, vertices, and edges."

• *It has 4 faces, 4 vertices, and 6 edges.*

"What is the name of this shape?"

• *Triangle-based pyramid.*

Tell students that this shape is also called a tetrahedron. *Tetra* means "four" and *hedron* means "face," so this is a 3-D shape with 4 triangle faces. Tell students that they are going to read about a building that is a tetrahedron, as well as a description of what it would be like to live in this building. As well, they are going to learn how to communicate effectively, in writing, about math topics.

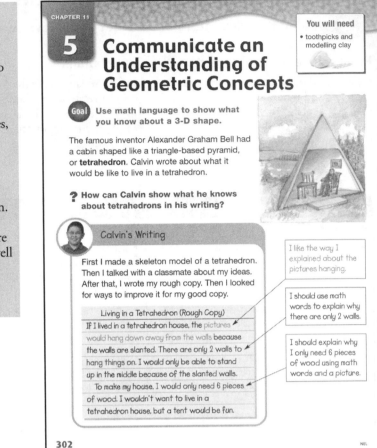

2. Teaching and Learning (Whole Class) ▶ 15–20 min

Read the paragraph about Alexander Graham Bell's cabin on Student Book page 302 and draw attention to the photo. Ask them if they have ever seen a house that looks like this. What do they think it would be like to live in such a house? Read Calvin's description of what it would be like to live in a tetrahedron. Point out the Communication Checklist on page 303 and Calvin's revisions to his rough draft, which are in the margin on Student Book page 302. Ask students to discuss the central question by answering prompts A and B. Be sure they explain their thinking using math language that includes faces, vertices, and edges.

Sample Discourse

"What improvements could Calvin make to his writing?"

• *Calvin should explain his thinking better by explaining why he would need 6 pieces of wood to build the skeleton model of the cabin. He should also say that these 6 pieces of wood would make the* edges *of the pyramid, where the faces join.*

• *Calvin could use more math language, such as the word* faces *when he says there are only 2 walls to hang things on, or* triangles *to describe the shapes of the walls and the floor.*

• *Calvin could write that the floor is the base of the tetrahedron, and he could draw a triangle to show it is the floor of the cabin.*

Reflecting

Use these questions to ensure that students are thinking about the process of writing, including the benefits of having other students read and respond to rough copies (first drafts) by evaluating Calvin's rough copy. Discuss the questions, encouraging different responses.

Sample Discourse

1. • *Discussing your ideas with someone else may give you more ideas.*
   • *Someone else may explain something to you.*
   • *Sometimes it's easier to understand things when you talk about them before writing.*

2. • *He knows that a tetrahedron has 6 edges.*
   • *He knows that the highest part of the tetrahedron is the vertex on the top.*

A. Use the Communication Checklist to decide how to improve Calvin's rough copy.
How would you answer each question in the checklist? Explain your thinking.

B. What changes could Calvin make when he writes his good copy?

Reflecting

1. Why is it helpful to talk with someone about your ideas?

2. What do Calvin's rough copy and comments show you about his knowledge of tetrahedrons?

Communication Checklist

☑ Did you explain your thinking?

☑ Did you use a model?

☑ Did you use math language?

Checking

3. Write about what it would be like to live in one of these buildings. Make a model of the shape. Talk with a classmate about your ideas before you write your rough copy.

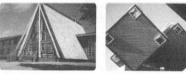

Cree Eco-Lodge on Moose Factory Island

Cube house in Toronto

Practising

4. Look at the rough copy you wrote for Question 3.
   a) What do you like about your writing?
   b) What could you do to improve your writing?
   c) Write your good copy.

Key Assessment of Learning Question. (See chart on next page.) 303

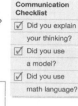

3. Consolidation ▸ 20–30 min

Checking (Individual/Pairs)

For intervention strategies, refer to the Meeting Individual Needs box or the Assessment for Feedback chart.

Give students experience with both types of building by having them work in pairs, with each student making a model of either the Cree Eco-Lodge or the Cube House.

Practising (Pairs)

If any students need extra support, provide them with copies of **Scaffolding Master p. 71**.

Closing (Whole Class)

Have students summarize their learning by asking "What are some of the best things you wrote in your paragraph?" Students can share the strengths of their good copies, both those ideas they included in their rough copy and those added after checking with the Communication Checklist. Have some students read their work out loud to the class.

Answers

A. For example,
- Calvin would explain why he needed only 6 pieces of wood to make a skeleton model. The 6 pieces of wood make up the edges, but do not include the faces (walls). He would need more wood if he were to add faces as well.
- Calvin could have included a drawing.
- Calvin could have used words such as *edges, faces,* and *vertex.*

B. For example, if I lived in a tetrahedron house, the pictures would hang down away from the *wall faces* because they are slanted. There are only 2 *wall faces* to hang things on because there are *4 faces* altogether and one is the door and one is the floor. I would only be able to stand up in the middle because of the slanted *wall faces.* To make my house, I would only need 6 pieces of wood *because a tetrahedron has only 6 edges.* I wouldn't want to live in a tetrahedron house, but a tent would be fun.

1. For example, when you discuss your ideas with others you can think more about your ideas and change them or add to them. You might also get more ideas from someone else. As well, you can see if your ideas make sense to someone else.

2. For example, Calvin knows there are 6 edges and 4 faces.

---

3. Cree Eco-Lodge
For example, in the Eco-Lodge it might be difficult to walk close to the walls. I would put furniture to sit on near the walls. I could build another floor halfway up the sides, or faces, of the house, to make more floor space. Maybe I could put my bed in this loft. It would be hard to hang lights from the ceiling because it is just an edge. Instead, I could put small lights along the walls. It would also be difficult to hang pictures on the side walls. I would have to hang them on the walls that are flat (the front or back faces of the prism) rather than the walls that are slanted.

4. a) For example, I like the way I used mathematical language, with words like faces and prism. I explained how hard it would be to hang lights from the ceiling by explaining that the ceiling is really only an edge.

b) For example, I could use more math words. I could explain that 2 of the faces of my Eco-Lodge are the same shape as the floor, but the other 2 faces are triangles.

c) For example, in the Eco-Lodge two faces meet at a top edge. The front vertex above the triangular entrance would be a good place to put a flag. I would put furniture to sit on, next to the rectangle faces of this pyramid, because they are slanted. I would have to hang pictures on the front or back faces of the triangle-based prism because these faces are not slanted. I could build another floor halfway up one face of the house to make more floor space. It would probably be easier to put lights along the faces of the lodge, rather than along the top edge.

Assessment Strategy: short answer
Communication

Key Assessment Question 4
• Look at the rough copy you wrote for Question 3.
a) What do you like about your writing?
b) What could you do to improve your writing?
c) Write your good copy.

1	2	3	4
• provides an incomplete and inaccurate explanation of what it would be like to live in the building	• provides a partial explanation of what it would be like to live in the building that exhibits some clarity and logical thought	• provides a complete, clear, and logical explanation of what it would be like to live in the building	• provides a thorough, clear, and insightful explanation of what it would be like to live in the building
• organization of written work is minimal and seriously impedes communication	• organization of written work is limited but does not seriously impede communication	• organization of written work is sufficient to support communication	• organization of written work is effective and aids communication
• uses very little mathematical vocabulary, and vocabulary used lacks clarity and precision	• uses a limited range of mathematical vocabulary with some degree of clarity and precision	• uses mathematical vocabulary with sufficient clarity and precision to communicate ideas	• uses a broad range of mathematical vocabulary
• makes a model that exhibits minimal clarity and accuracy, and is ineffective in communicating	• makes a model that lacks clarity and accuracy, though not sufficient to impede communication	• makes a model that is sufficiently clear and accurate to communicate	• makes a model that is clear, precise, and effective in communicating

Extra Practice and Extension

• You might assign any of the questions related to this lesson, which are cross-referenced in the chart below.

Chapter Review	Student Book p. 317, Question 5
Workbook	p. 98, all questions
Nelson Web Site	Visit **www.mathk8.nelson.com** and follow the links to *Nelson Mathematics 4*, Chapter 11.

At Home

• Suggest students write a description of their own home using math language. They could also make a skeleton model of their home.

Extra Support:
Scaffolding Master for Lesson 5 p. 71

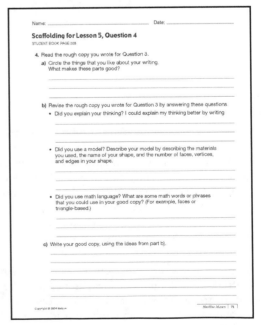

Math Background

There is a variety of books on architecture and the built environment that provide good photographs of old and contemporary architecture, and would be suitable for children to examine and discuss or write about, in terms of the mathematical/geometric concepts.

Many children (and adults) have little experience with writing about mathematical ideas, and see math as a subject in which numbers or one-word answers are the only important types of communication. Modelling examples of effective mathematical writing helps students develop good communication skills. The use of the Communication Checklist provides students with structure for writing and revising mathematical concepts and processes.

Mid-Chapter Review

Using the Mid-Chapter Review

Use this page to assess students' understanding of the concepts developed in the chapter so far. Refer to the assessment chart on the next page for details of each question.

Materials: (optional) 3-D models of prisms and pyramids illustrated in Question 1
(optional) skeleton models of shapes in Question 3

Answers

1.

3-D shape and name	Drawing of 2-D faces	Number of vertices	Number of edges
triangle-based prism	△△▢▢▢	6	9
square-based prism (cube)	▢▢▢▢▢▢	8	12
rectangle-based prism	▢▢▢▢▢▢	8	12
square-based pyramid	▢△△△△	5	8
triangle-based pyramid	△△△△	4	6

2. a) There are always more edges than vertices.

   b) Similarities: both are named after the shape that forms their base(s). For example, a triangle-based prism and a triangle-based pyramid both have triangle bases. Differences: prisms have 2 congruent bases that are connected with rectangular faces. Pyramids only have 1 base and their other faces are triangular and join at a central vertex.

   c) The cube and triangle-based pyramid (tetrahedron) have all congruent faces.

3. a) 8 straws

   b) 9 straws

   c) 10 straws

   d) 18 straws

4.

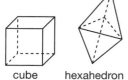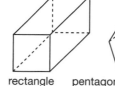

cube   hexahedron   rectangle   pentagon-based pyramid

Possible shapes include: a cube, a rectangle-based prism, a pentagon-based pyramid, and a hexahedron (2 tetrahedrons that share a base).

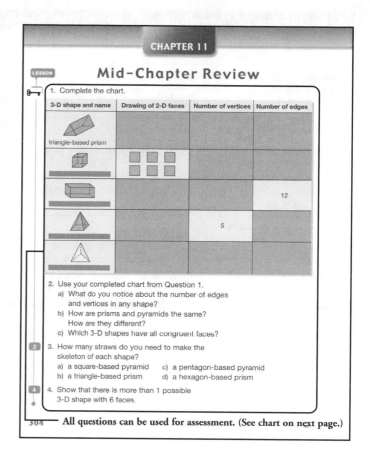

Mid-Chapter Review

1. Complete the chart.

3-D shape and name	Drawing of 2-D faces	Number of vertices	Number of edges
triangle-based prism			
			12
		5	

2. Use your completed chart from Question 1.
   a) What do you notice about the number of edges and vertices in any shape?
   b) How are prisms and pyramids the same? How are they different?
   c) Which 3-D shapes have all congruent faces?

3. How many straws do you need to make the skeleton of each shape?
   a) a square-based pyramid   c) a pentagon-based pyramid
   b) a triangle-based prism   d) a hexagon-based prism

4. Show that there is more than 1 possible 3-D shape with 6 faces.

304   **All questions can be used for assessment. (See chart on next page.)**

Assessment of Learning—What to Look for in Student Work...

Assessment Strategy: written question
Understanding of Concepts, Application of Procedures

Question 1
• Complete the chart.

1	2	3	4
Understanding of Concepts			
• demonstrates superficial or inaccurate understanding of the 2-dimensional shapes of the faces of 3-dimensional shapes, and the names of 3-D shapes	• demonstrates a growing but still incomplete understanding of the 2-dimensional shapes of the faces of 3-dimensional shapes, and the names of 3-D shapes	• demonstrates grade-appropriate understanding of the 2-dimensional shapes of the faces of 3-dimensional shapes, and the names of 3-D shapes	• demonstrates in-depth understanding of the 2-dimensional shapes of the faces of 3-dimensional shapes, and the names of 3-D shapes
Application of Procedures			
• makes major errors and/or omissions when sketching the 2-D faces and identifying the number of vertices and edges	• makes several errors and/or omissions when sketching the 2-D faces and identifying the number of vertices and edges	• makes only a few minor errors and/or omissions when sketching the 2-D faces and identifying the number of vertices and edges	• makes almost no errors when sketching the 2-D faces and identifying the number of vertices and edges

Assessment Strategy: written question
Understanding of Concepts, Communication

Question 2
• Use your completed chart from Question 1.
a) What do you notice about the number of edges and vertices in any shape?
b) How are prisms and pyramids the same? How are they different?
c) Which 3-D shapes have all congruent faces?

1	2	3	4
Understanding of Concepts			
• has difficulty connecting new concepts to prior learning	• demonstrates a limited ability to connect new concepts to prior learning	• demonstrates a growing ability to connect new concepts to prior learning	• easily connects new concepts to prior learning
Communication			
• provides incomplete or inaccurate descriptions that lack clarity and logical thought using very little mathematical vocabulary	• provides partial descriptions that exhibit some clarity and logical thought using a limited range of mathematical vocabulary	• provides complete, clear, and logical descriptions of geometric properties and relationships using appropriate mathematical vocabulary	• provides thorough, clear, and insightful descriptions of geometric properties and relationships using a broad range of mathematical vocabulary

Assessment Strategy: short answer
Application of Procedures

Question 3
• How many straws do you need to make the skeleton of each shape?
a) a square-based pyramid
b) a triangle-based prism
c) a pentagon-based pyramid
d) a hexagon-based prism
(Score correct responses out of 4.)

Assessment Strategy: written question
Problem Solving

Question 4
• Show that there is more than 1 possible 3-D shape with 6 faces.

1	2	3	4
• uses a strategy and attempts to solve problem but does not arrive at an answer	• carries out a plan to some extent, using a strategy, and develops a partial and/or incorrect solution	• carries out a plan effectively by using an appropriate strategy and solving the problem	• shows flexibility and insight by trying and adapting 1 or more strategies to solve the problem

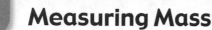

Goal Estimate, measure, and record the mass of objects.

Prerequisite Skills/Concepts

- Use balance scales to compare relative mass of 2 objects.
- Use estimation to compare sums of numbers to a target rounded number.
- Use rounding to tens and hundreds places.

Expectations

4m34 demonstrate an understanding of and ability to apply appropriate metric prefixes in measurement and estimation activities

4m38 estimate, measure, and record the [capacity of containers and the] mass of familiar objects, compare the measures, [and model the volume of three-dimensional figures]

4m58 estimate, measure, and record the mass of objects using standard units, compare the measures, and order objects by mass

Assessment for Feedback	What You Will See Students Doing...	
Students will	**When Students Understand**	**If Students Misunderstand**
• use a balance scale to find the mass of common classroom objects	• Students will check to ensure the scale is calibrated accurately and choose the appropriate metric mass to balance the object.	• Students having difficulty using the balances and measuring mass would benefit from a demonstration.
• find the total mass (in grams) of a variety of objects and choose combinations of items that will be close to 2 kg and 6 kg	• Students will be able to calculate the mass of the items and suggest appropriate items for backpacks no more than 2 kg and 6 kg.	• If students are unsure of the process required, work through an example after reviewing prompts B to E.
• explain the relationship between grams and kilograms	• Students will explain that 1 kg is the same as 1000 g. Some students may refer to place value in their explanations.	• For students having difficulty, use balance scales to demonstrate that a combination of smaller masses with a sum of 1000 g balances a 1 kg mass.

Preparation and Planning

Pacing	5–10 min Introduction 30–40 min Teaching and Learning 5–10 min Consolidation
Materials	• 1 kg sugar, 500 g box of cereal, a bag with 5 g of salt (or items with similar weight) • 1 balance scales and set of masses/group or class
Masters	• Mental Math, p. 64 • List of Food and Clothing Master p. 74
Workbook	p. 99
Vocabulary/ Symbols	mass, balance scales, gram (g), kilogram (kg)
Key Assessment of Learning Question	Entire exploration, Problem Solving

Meeting Individual Needs

Extra Challenge

- Students could create an ordered list of the masses of objects in their desks.
- Students could find the sum of the masses of objects in their own backpacks.

Extra Support

- Provide more time for students to practise measuring and recording the masses of common classroom objects.

1. Introduction (Whole Class)
▶ 5–10 min

Show students a 1 kg of sugar, a 500 g of box of cereal, and a bag with 5 g of salt (about a teaspoon). Before you show them these items, cover up the masses listed on the containers. Draw attention to the vocabulary box, and then ask students which item has the greatest mass. Demonstrate the use of the balance scales to find the mass of each item. To get a sense of mass, have students stand with arms straight out to their sides holding the box of cereal in one hand and something with a similar mass (such as a small book) in the other. Tell students they will be finding objects in the classroom with masses of about 5 g, 500 g, and 1 kg. They should estimate mass by comparing the items in their hands, against the mass of sugar, cereal and/or salt. After estimating, they can use balance scales.

2. Teaching and Learning (Small Groups/Whole Class) ▶ 30–40 min

Read together the paragraph "Shani's Backpack". Help students make a list of the important information about mass that is in this paragraph to model a strategy for reading informational text. Draw attention to the central question. Provide balance scales and masses, and have groups complete prompt A. For prompt B, students may create their own list or use the list provided on the Food and Clothing List Master. The more experience students have with finding the masses of objects themselves the better. Share the results of this exploration with the class by creating a class list of the objects and their masses.

Sample Discourse
"What objects did you find with a mass of about 5 grams? About 500 g? About 1 kg?"
* *My pencil, but it was more than 5 g.*
* *My big pencil box with all my felts and crayons was the closest thing to 500 g, but it was only 460 g.*
* *We put three textbooks together and they were really close to 1 kg.*

"What were the total masses of the items in the 2 backpacks?"
* *When we added Shani's things to her brother's backpack we got a total mass of 7937 grams, which is the same as 7 kilograms and 937 grams, so it is less than 8 kilograms.*

Reflecting

Use these questions to ensure that students understand the relationship between grams and kilograms. Help them develop a sense of the relative masses of common classroom objects. Encourage students to use the balance scales again to check their estimates, and to include a wide variety of objects. Discuss the questions, encouraging different responses.

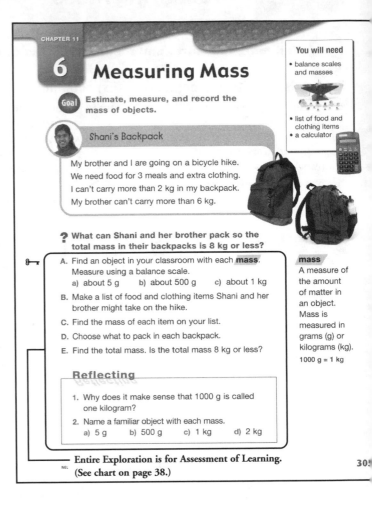

6 Measuring Mass

Goal Estimate, measure, and record the mass of objects.

You will need
* balance scales and masses
* list of food and clothing items
* a calculator

Shani's Backpack

My brother and I are going on a bicycle hike. We need food for 3 meals and extra clothing. I can't carry more than 2 kg in my backpack. My brother can't carry more than 6 kg.

? What can Shani and her brother pack so the total mass in their backpacks is 8 kg or less?

A. Find an object in your classroom with each **mass**. Measure using a balance scale.
 a) about 5 g b) about 500 g c) about 1 kg

B. Make a list of food and clothing items Shani and her brother might take on the hike.

C. Find the mass of each item on your list.

D. Choose what to pack in each backpack.

E. Find the total mass. Is the total mass 8 kg or less?

Reflecting

1. Why does it make sense that 1000 g is called one kilogram?

2. Name a familiar object with each mass.
 a) 5 g b) 500 g c) 1 kg d) 2 kg

mass
A measure of the amount of matter in an object. Mass is measured in grams (g) or kilograms (kg).
1000 g = 1 kg

Entire Exploration is for Assessment of Learning. (See chart on page 38.)

NEL

305

Sample Discourse
1. • Kilo *always means "1000," so 1 kg is the same as 1000 g.*
2. a) • *My highlighter felt pen is about 5 g.*
   b) • *My shoes weigh about 500 kg.*
   c) • *My library books weigh about 1 kg.*
   d) • *The big class encyclopaedia weighs about 2 kg.*

Related Questions to Ask

Ask	Possible Response
About **Question B:** • Why does the total mass for Shani need to be 2 kg or less, and for her brother 6 kg or less?	• *Because Shani can't carry more than 2 kg and her brother can't carry more than 6 kg*
About all questions • Why do we always need to write the unit beside the number when we record the mass of an object?	• *There is a big difference between the sizes of standard units. For example, 20 g is not the same as 20 kg.*

Answers

A. For example:

   a) a house key

   b) several hardcover textbooks

   c) a litre of water

B. See List of Food and Clothing Master for sample list items.

C. See List of Food and Clothing Master for sample masses.

D. Shani's backpack can include any combination of items that is equal to or less than 2 kg. For example, it could include water, a T-shirt, cereal, a can of milk, and peanut butter. Shani's brother's backpack can include any combination of items that is equal to or less than 6 kg. For example, it could include water, a T-shirt, hot dogs, hot dog buns, pasta dinner, granola bars, crackers, a cold pack, a towel, apples, a can of soup, a loaf of bread, a can of beans, seeds and nuts, and rice.

E. Students' answers may vary, but all should be less than 8 kg. The total mass of the items in prompt E, for example, is equal to 7937 g (7 kg 937 g) based on the following masses.

	0 g to 249 g	250 g to 499 g	500 g to 749 g	750 g to 1 kg
T-shirt	62 g			
cereal	50 g			
sweatshirt	62 g			
pasta dinner	200 g			
granola bars	170 g			
crackers	220 g			
apples	215 g			
seeds and nuts	75 g			
rice	165 g			
peanut butter		250 g		
hot dogs		450 g		
cold pack		345 g		
towel		378 g		
can of milk			625 g	
hot dog buns			675 g	
can of soup			640 g	
loaf of bread			675 g	
can of beans			680 g	
1 L water				1 kg

1. It makes sense that 1000 g equals 1 kg, because *kilo* means "1000."

2. For example,

   a) my key is about 5 g

   b) my math book is about 500 g

   c) 1 L of milk is about 1 kg

   d) a full 2 L of pop is about 2 kg

3. Consolidation ▸ 5–10 min

For intervention strategies, refer to the Meeting Individual Needs box and the Assessment for Feedback chart.

Closing (Whole Class)

Have students summarize their learning by asking them, "What have you learned about measuring the mass of classroom objects?" They can write their responses in their math journals.

- *I learned that the mass of most of the things inside my desk is less than 1 kg, and some things are less than 10 g.*

- *I was surprised to learn that 1 kg is heavier than I thought it was. I thought my big dictionary would weigh at least a kilogram, but I learned that it only has a mass of about 450 g.*

- *I know that when I put all my homework and my lunch bag and my gym shoes in my backpack I have to carry almost 2 kg on my back.*

Assessment Strategy: investigation
Problem Solving

Assessment Opportunity
In this exploration lesson, the entire investigation is an opportunity for assessment. You will see students carrying out an inquiry and will be able to observe their ability to use balance scales and masses to estimate, measure, and record the mass of objects and to use their results to choose items to pack backpacks.

To gather evidence about a student's ability to problem solve, use informal observation, questioning, and written work. Use the Problem Solving Rubric (Tool 6) to help you focus on the problem-solving process. You may wish to focus on the "Carry Out the Plan" and "Look Back" rows in the rubric.

Extra Practice and Extension

- You might assign any of the questions related to this lesson, which are cross-referenced in the chart below.

Skills Bank	Student Book p. 313, Question 5
Problem Bank	Student Book pp. 314–315, Questions 6,7,8, & 9
Chapter Review	Student Book p. 317, Questions 6 & 7
Workbook	p. 99, all questions
Nelson Web Site	Visit **www.mathk8.nelson.com** and follow the links to *Nelson Mathematics 4*, Chapter 11.

At Home

- Encourage students to find some objects at home that are similar to the ones they at school. Have them estimate the mass and bring 1 or 2 objects to school to measure the mass and compare the mass to their estimate.

Math Background

Many children still hear imperial measurement units being used at home for capacity (e.g., cups) and mass (e.g., pounds), so it is very important to give students many opportunities to measure a variety of objects using metric scales and units. Although their parents may have explained how to convert from imperial to metric, students need to develop their own internal sense of what it means to have a mass of 5 g, 100 g, 500 g, 1 kg, 10 kg, and so on. These benchmarks will help them in estimating probable masses, which is an important skill for solving contextualized problems involving mass.

Common Misconceptions: When asked to estimate the closest number to a target number, students will often select the closest number that is *less* than the target, overlooking a greater number that is even closer to the target. The need to consider numbers "greater than" as well as "less than" often needs direct instruction. However, in the context of this lesson, in which students are told that they can't have a number of objects with a mass of more than 8 kg, students need to consider the context of this problem. This is a good opportunity to reinforce the need to fully understand the context of a problem when designing a plan to solve it.

7 Measuring Capacity

Goal Estimate, measure, and record the capacity of containers.

Prerequisite Skills/Concepts

- Recognize when to apply measurement terms *millilitre* and *litre*.
- Understand how the shape of the container may influence estimated volume.

Expectations

4m34 demonstrate an understanding of and ability to apply appropriate metric prefixes in measurement and estimation activities

4m35 identify relationships between and among measurement concepts

4m36 solve problems related to their day-to-day environment using measurement and estimation

4m38 estimate, measure, and record the capacity of containers [and the mass of familiar objects], compare the measures, and model the volume of three-dimensional figures

4m56 select the most appropriate standard unit to measure the capacity of containers

Assessment for Feedback	What You Will See Students Doing...	
Students will	**When Students Understand**	**If Students Misunderstand**
• estimate and measure the capacity of containers	• Students will successfully estimate the capacity of a variety of containers.	• Students may have difficulty estimating because of assumptions they have made based on the shapes of containers. Give these students more chances to explore containers with irregular shapes, such as flower vases and drinking glasses.
• understand that 1000 mL = 1 L	• Students will use the correct prefixes when recording their measurements.	• Students may have trouble recording using appropriate metric prefixes. They may need assurance that 2.225 L is the same as 2225 mL and need assistance to determine when to use L and when to use mL. You could show them the labels of various containers to see how capacity is recorded.

Preparation and Planning

Pacing	**10–15 min** Introduction **25–35 min** Teaching and Learning **10–15 min** Consolidation
Materials	• 1 L bottle and 250 mL measuring cup/small group of students • a variety of other containers including a drinking glass and a mug • water • 1 funnel/small group of students
Masters	• Mental Math, p. 64
Workbook	p. 100, all questions
Vocabulary/Symbols	capacity, millilitres, litres
Key Assessment of Learning Question	Entire exploration, Problem Solving

Meeting Individual Needs

Extra Challenge

- Challenge students to record their water consumption over a period of days. Give students a purpose for measuring the water intake. For example, in health class, students learn that they should drink from 1 L to 2 L of water each day.
- Have students record in their math journals the different ways in which they (or family members) make measurements at home during the course of 1 week. For example, using measuring spoons, cups, a scale, and so on.

Extra Support

- Show students the volume on the labels of various containers. Also, teach them other ways to determine capacity. For example, estimate by comparing the size and shape of a given container to another with a known volume such as a 250 mL measuring cup. Then, imagine how many of the known containers would fit inside the new container. Students could also pour the liquid from a container that does not show the capacity on its label to a container that is labelled, then compare the capacity of the 2 containers.

1. Introduction (Small Groups)
▶ 10–15 min

Show students containers of various sizes and shapes. Draw attention to the vocabulary box on Student Book page 306. Ask students to read the capacities on the containers' labels (if they exist) and order the containers from least to greatest capacity. Establish the relationship, related to other metric measures, that there are 1000 mL in 1 L. Tell students they will be measuring the capacity of a variety of containers.

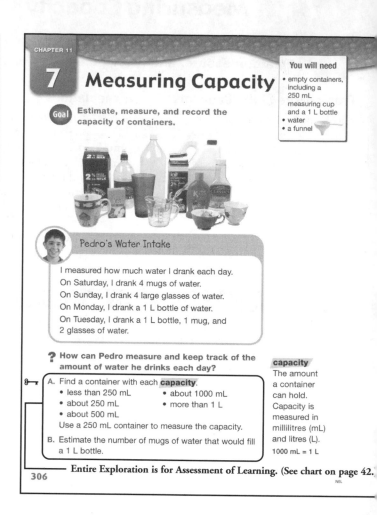

CHAPTER 11

7 Measuring Capacity

Goal Estimate, measure, and record the capacity of containers.

You will need
• empty containers, including a 250 mL measuring cup and a 1 L bottle
• water
• a funnel

Pedro's Water Intake

I measured how much water I drank each day.
On Saturday, I drank 4 mugs of water.
On Sunday, I drank 4 large glasses of water.
On Monday, I drank a 1 L bottle of water.
On Tuesday, I drank a 1 L bottle, 1 mug, and 2 glasses of water.

? How can Pedro measure and keep track of the amount of water he drinks each day?

A. Find a container with each **capacity**.
 • less than 250 mL   • about 1000 mL
 • about 250 mL   • more than 1 L
 • about 500 mL
 Use a 250 mL container to measure the capacity.

B. Estimate the number of mugs of water that would fill a 1 L bottle.

capacity
The amount a container can hold. Capacity is measured in millilitres (mL) and litres (L).
1000 mL = 1 L

306

— Entire Exploration is for Assessment of Learning. (See chart on page 42.

NEL

2. Teaching and Learning (Small Groups) ▶ 25–35 min

Set up several workstations. Each station will need a glass (about 500 mL), a mug (about 250 mL), a 1 L water bottle, water, and several other containers such as a tea cup, an empty juice box, an empty frozen juice container, and so on. Read the page together, drawing attention to the central question. Have the students work in small groups to complete prompts A to F. Have students post their results on chart paper.

Sample Discourse

"How did you figure out how much water Pedro drank in any given day?"
• *We figured out that about 4 mugs can fill a litre bottle, so each mug holds about 250 mL because 250 mL times 4 equals 1000 mL, and that's the same as 1 L.*
• *A large glass is equal to about 2 mugs, so that would equal about 500 mL. We figured that out because 250 mL times 2 equals 500 mL.*

Reflecting

Use these questions to ensure that students understand how to measure capacity. Discuss the questions, encouraging different responses.

Sample Discourse

2. a) *closer to the bottom than the top; for example, because the bottom part is bigger than the top part*

 b) *halfway between; for example, because the container is even all the way from top to bottom*

 c) *closer to the top than the bottom, because the bottom is very narrow and won't hold that much water*

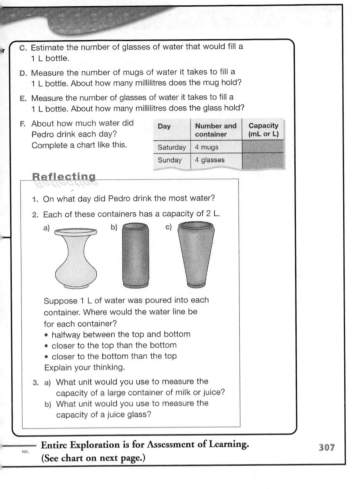

C. Estimate the number of glasses of water that would fill a 1 L bottle.

D. Measure the number of mugs of water it takes to fill a 1 L bottle. About how many millilitres does the mug hold?

E. Measure the number of glasses of water it takes to fill a 1 L bottle. About how many millilitres does the glass hold?

F. About how much water did Pedro drink each day? Complete a chart like this.

Day	Number and container	Capacity (mL or L)
Saturday	4 mugs	
Sunday	4 glasses	

Reflecting

1. On what day did Pedro drink the most water?

2. Each of these containers has a capacity of 2 L.

   a) b) c)

   Suppose 1 L of water was poured into each container. Where would the water line be for each container?
   • halfway between the top and bottom
   • closer to the top than the bottom
   • closer to the bottom than the top
   Explain your thinking.

3. a) What unit would you use to measure the capacity of a large container of milk or juice?
   b) What unit would you use to measure the capacity of a juice glass?

Entire Exploration is for Assessment of Learning. (See chart on next page.)

307

For intervention strategies, refer to the Meeting Individual Needs box and the Assessment for Feedback chart.

Closing (Whole Class)

Have students summarize their learning by asking them to write in their journals their responses to the question "What are some things to remember when you measure or estimate the capacity of a container?"

• *Don't be tricked by the shape of containers. A tall, skinny container can hold the same amount as a short, fat container.*

• *You can use the capacity of a container that you know the size of to estimate the capacity of a new container.*

• *Some containers have their capacity written on them.*

• *Whether you choose millilitres and litres as the units you use to record capacity depends on the size of the container and its capacity.*

Answers

A. For example, less than 250 mL—small yogurt container, juice tetra pack; about 250 mL—whipped-cream carton, small cottage cheese container; about 500 mL—water or juice bottle, medium-sized margarine tub; about 1000 mL—waxed milk container, bottle of soda; more than 1 L—oil bottle, ketchup bottle.

B. Approximately 4 mugs.

C. Approximately 2 glasses.

D. It should takes about 4 mugs to fill a 1 L bottle. Each mug holds about 250 mL.

E. It takes about 2 glasses to fill a 1 L bottle. Each glass holds about 500 mL.

F. **Pedro's Daily Water Intake**

Day	Number and containers	Capacity (mL or L)
Saturday	4 mugs	1000 mL or 1 L
Sunday	4 glasses	2000 mL or 2 L
Monday	1 bottle	1 L
Tuesday	1 bottle, 1 mug, 2 glasses	2250 mL

1L   250   1L

1. Tuesday. 1 bottle (1 L) + 1 mug (250 mL) + 2 glasses (500 mL) = 2250 mL.

2. a) closer to the bottom than the top
   b) halfway between the top and bottom
   c) closer to the top than the bottom

3. a) litres (L)
   b) millilitres (mL)

mug = 250mL
1 glass = approx 500mL

Assessment of Learning—What to Look for in Student Work...

Assessment Strategy: investigation
Problem Solving

Assessment Opportunity
In this exploration lesson, the entire investigation is an opportunity for assessment. You will see students carrying out an inquiry and will be able to observe their ability to use empty containers, including a 250 mL measuring cup and a 1 L bottle, to estimate, measure, and record the capacity of objects and to use their results to calculate the amount of water that is drunk each day.

To gather evidence about a student's ability to problem solve, use informal observation, questioning, and written work. Use the Problem Solving Rubric (Tool 6) to help you focus on the problem-solving process. You may want to focus on the "Carry Out the Plan," "Look Back," and "Communicate" rows in the rubric.

Extra Practice and Extension

- You might assign any of the questions related to this lesson, which are cross-referenced in the chart below.

Skills Bank	Student Book p. 313, Question 6
Problem Bank	Student Book p. 315, Question 10
Chapter Review	Student Book p. 317, Question 8
Workbook	p. 100, all questions
Nelson Web Site	Visit **www.mathk8.nelson.com** and follow the links to *Nelson Mathematics 4*, Chapter 11.

Math Background

Students may benefit from a review on how to measure liquids accurately, looking at the measuring cup or container at eye level to ensure it is full. Any extra time that can be provided to students to continue their hands-on exploration of capacity will strengthen student learning. Most students have a good understanding of what 1 L is, but often are less confident with millilitre measurements.

At Home

- Students can look at home for a favourite recipe, and make it with the help of a family member.

8 Using Mass and Capacity

Goal **Choose appropriate capacity and mass units.**

Prerequisite Skills/Concepts

- Estimate, measure, and record the mass of objects.
- Estimate, measure, and record the capacity of containers.

Expectations

4m35 identify relationships between and among measurement concepts

4m36 solve problems related to their day-to-day environment using measurement and estimation

4m38 estimate [measure,]and record the capacity of containers and [the mass of familiar objects] compare the measures [and model the volume of three dimensional figures]

4m56 select the most appropriate standard unit to measure the capacity of containers

4m59 select the most appropriate standard unit to measure mass

4m60 describe the relationship between grams and kilograms and millilitres and litres

Assessment for Feedback	What You Will See Students Doing...	
Students will	**When Students Understand**	**If Students Misunderstand**
• read the ingredients and specific measurements in a pancake recipe • choose appropriate units	• Students will answer questions correctly, referring to the recipe to find exact information if necessary. • Students will answer the questions correctly and can explain their reasoning, using their knowledge about equivalent measures of capacity and mass.	• Students may need to refer to measuring tools (cups, spoons, scales) to gauge mass and capacity. • Students may not initially see the relationship between 2 mL and 2 L of salt and 1 g and 1 kg of chocolate chips. Point out the relationships and help students to find the equivalences (e.g., 2 L = 2000 mL of salt; 1 kg = 1000 g of chocolate chips).

Preparation and Planning

Pacing	**10–15 min** Introduction **15–20 min** Teaching and Learning **15–25 min** Consolidation
Materials	• plastic grocery bag • several canned and boxed food items • (optional) balance scales (1/small group of students) • (optional) 1 set of measuring cups and spoons (1/group)
Masters	• Mental Math, p. 64
Workbook	p. 101, all questions
Vocabulary/ Symbols	mass, capacity, length, width, diameter
Key Assessment of Learning Question	Question 7, Understanding of Concepts

Meeting Individual Needs

Extra Challenge

- Each student could bring in one box or container that has numerical data on it (e.g., mass, capacity, dietary information). Challenge students to write questions (and answers) regarding measurement that other students could try to answer.

Extra Support

- Bring in measuring cups and spoons for those students who have difficulty understanding the capacity of measurements just by reading the recipe.

1. Introduction (Whole Class)
⬧ 10–15 min

Fill a plastic grocery bag with objects until it has a mass of about 1 kg. Ask students how they would estimate the mass. How could they check their estimate? How could they adjust the objects until they are closer to a kilogram?

Sort the items in the bag into 2 groups: items that are measured by mass and items that are measured by capacity. Explain that dry items are usually measured by mass and liquid items are usually measured by capacity. Remind students of these relationships: 1 L = 2000 mL and 1 kg = 1000 g.

Tell students that they are going to use units for mass and capacity.

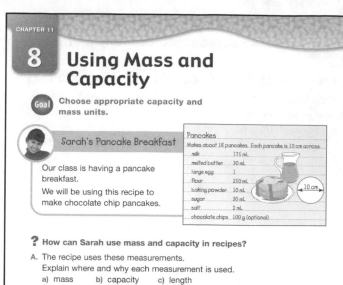

8 Using Mass and Capacity

Goal Choose appropriate capacity and mass units.

Sarah's Pancake Breakfast

Our class is having a pancake breakfast.
We will be using this recipe to make chocolate chip pancakes.

Pancakes
Makes about 16 pancakes. Each pancake is 10 cm across.

milk	175 mL
melted butter	30 mL
large egg	1
flour	250 mL
baking powder	10 mL
sugar	30 mL
salt	2 mL
chocolate chips	100 g (optional)

? How can Sarah use mass and capacity in recipes?

A. The recipe uses these measurements.
   Explain where and why each measurement is used.
   a) mass   b) capacity   c) length

B. Why is the milk measured in millilitres rather than litres?

C. Why are the chocolate chips measured in grams rather than kilograms?

D. Suppose 2 L of salt and 1 kg of chocolate chips were used by accident to make the pancakes.
   a) What would happen?
   b) How do you know these are unreasonable amounts?

E. One of Sarah's classmates thinks 1 mL of maple syrup and 500 kg of butter should be served with the pancakes. Are these amounts reasonable? Explain your thinking.

308

NEL

2. Teaching and Learning (Small Groups) ⬧ 15–20 min

Talk to students about their experiences with cooking or baking. Draw attention to the central question and ask students to explain the difference between mass and capacity. Remind them to work in groups to answer the prompts A to E.

Sample Discourse

"Which measuring tool would you use to measure 30 mL of melted butter?"

• *You could use the 15 mL measure twice, since 2 × 15 mL = 30 mL.*

• *You could use a 30 mL measure.*

Reflecting

Use these questions to ensure that students have reflected on the importance of knowing how to measure. Discuss the questions and encourage a variety of responses and examples.

Sample Discourse

1. • *If you make the pancakes bigger, you won't get 16 pancakes from the recipe.*

   • *You can estimate how many pancakes you can fit in a pan at once.*

2. • *You need to know what units to use and how many units you need. For example, the milk is measured in millilitres and you need to measure 175.*

   • *You need to know the number of units so you can choose what to measure with. I could measure the milk in a 250 mL measuring cup.*

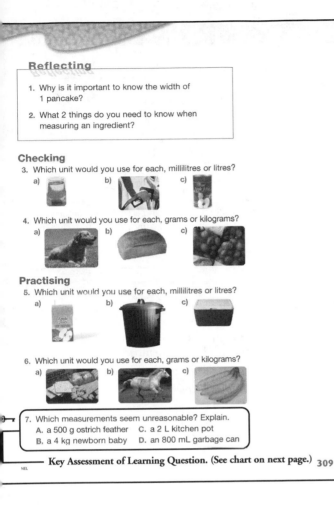

Reflecting

1. Why is it important to know the width of 1 pancake?

2. What 2 things do you need to know when measuring an ingredient?

Checking

3. Which unit would you use for each, millilitres or litres?
   a)   b)   c)

4. Which unit would you use for each, grams or kilograms?
   a)   b)   c)

Practising

5. Which unit would you use for each, millilitres or litres?
   a)   b)   c)

6. Which unit would you use for each, grams or kilograms?
   a)   b)   c)

7. Which measurements seem unreasonable? Explain.
   A. a 500 g ostrich feather   C. a 2 L kitchen pot
   B. a 4 kg newborn baby   D. an 800 mL garbage can

Key Assessment of Learning Question. (See chart on next page.) 309

3. Consolidation ▶ 15–25 min

Checking (Pairs)

For intervention strategies, refer to the Meeting Individual Needs box or the Assessment for Feedback chart.

3. & 4. Encourage students to refer to the measuring tools to help them choose the appropriate responses.

3. c) Students may not be sure whether this is a large or small can of juice. So, either millilitre or litre could be a correct answer, but ensure that students can explain their rationale.

Practising (Individual)

5. & 6. Ask students to explain their reasoning to check their understanding.

7. Encourage students to reflect back to the introductory activity (where 1 kg of items were put in a grocery bag). For example, it doesn't make sense for the ostrich feather to weigh about half of what the grocery bag weighed.

Closing (Whole Class)

Have students summarize what they have learned by asking, "What did you learn about measuring mass and capacity when you were solving Sarah's problem?"

- *Large items are usually measured in kilograms.*
- *Items with a large capacity are usually measured in litres.*
- *A large number of smaller items (e.g., potatoes) are usually measured in kilograms.*

Answers

A. a) For example, mass is used to measure chocolate chips. This ensures the correct amount of chocolate chips is used in the recipe.

b) Capacity is used to measure all of the ingredients except the egg and chocolate chips. This tells students the size of the measuring implement needed.

c) Length is used when giving the size (width or diameter) of the pancakes so that you know how big the pancakes will be.

B. For example, millilitres are used because the amount of milk needed is less than one litre.

C. For example, grams are used because the amount of chocolate chips needed is less than one kilogram.

D. For example,

a) The pancakes wouldn't come out right because 2 L of salt and 1 kg of chocolate chips are much more than the recipe requires. The pancakes would be runny and inedible because the chocolate would melt and they'd be too salty to eat.

b) They are much larger amounts than the recipe calls for (1000 times more salt and 10 times more chocolate).

E. For example, these are unreasonable amounts because 500 kg of butter is heavier than a person like me, and I like more maple syrup than 1 mL.

1. So you know how much batter to pour in the pan. If you estimate the diameter as you keep pouring in the batter, you'd stop when the pancake measured about 10 cm across.

2. You need to know the units of measure and how many of these units.

3. a) millilitre   **b)** litre   **c)** millilitre or litre

4. a) kilogram   **b)** gram   **c)** kilogram

5. a) millilitre   **b)** litre   **c)** litre

6. a) gram   **b)** kilogram   **c)** gram

7. The measurements in A and D seem unreasonable because a feather is very light, and 500 g is too much for one feather to weigh. A garbage can has a large capacity and 800 mL is less than 1 L.

Assessment of Learning—What to Look for in Student Work...

Assessment Strategy: short answer
Understanding of Concepts

Key Assessment Question 7

- Which measurements seem unreasonable? Explain.
  A. a 500 g ostrich feather
  B. a 4 kg newborn baby
  C. a 2 L kitchen pot
  D. an 800 L garbage can

(Score 1 point for each correct response and 1 point for each appropriate explanation, for a total of 8.)

1	2	3	4
• has difficulty connecting new concepts (capacity and mass units) to prior learning (appropriate choice of measurement)	• demonstrates a limited ability to connect new concepts (capacity and mass units) to prior learning (appropriate choice of measurement)	• demonstrates a growing ability to connect new concepts (capacity and mass units) to prior learning (appropriate choice of measurement)	• easily connects new concepts (capacity and mass units) to prior learning (appropriate choice of measurement)

Extra Practice and Extension

- You might assign any of the questions related to this lesson, which are cross-referenced in the chart below.

Skills Bank	Student Book p. 313, Questions 7, 8, & 9
Problem Bank	Student Book p. 315, Question 11
Chapter Review	Student Book p. 317, Question 9
Workbook	p. 101, all questions
Nelson Web Site	Visit **www.mathk8.nelson.com** and follow the links to *Nelson Mathematics 4*, Chapter 11.

Math Background

Although dry baking supplies are usually packaged for sale by mass, when such dry ingredients are measured out for recipes, they are usually measured by capacity for reasons of convenience; it is more practical to measure with measuring spoons or cups in millilitres than with a scale in grams. This would probably be true for the chocolate chips as well. In this case, it would be a bit less than a cup.

At Home

- Students can take home the pancake recipe and try it out, serving the pancakes to family members.
- Students can bring in favourite family recipes to share. They could put together a class book of recipes.

9 Modelling Volume

 Goal Model 3-D shapes to measure volume.

Prerequisite Skills/Concepts

- Identify rows and columns in 2-D grids and 3-D prisms.
- Identify a 3-D shape, viewed from more than one perspective, as the same shape.
- Identify length, width, and height.

Expectations

4m38 [estimate, measure, and record the capacity of containers and the mass of familiar objects, compare the measures, and] model the volume of three-dimensional figures

4m57 model three-dimensional figures of specific volumes using blocks

Assessment for Feedback	What You Will See Students Doing...	
Students will	**When Students Understand**	**If Students Misunderstand**
• use linking cubes to create models that represent prisms	• Students will use linking cubes to model the 3-D shape of another prism.	• Students may have difficulty making a model of the prism. Ensure that they choose a simple prism and partner them with another student for assistance.
• determine the volume of the modelled prisms	• Students will count the cubes to determine the volume.	• Students may have difficulty with the new word *volume*. Ensure that they understand that, in this lesson, volume is the number of cubes in their prism.
• record their work using drawings and measurement and geometry words	• Students will record their work using a combination of top view ("bird's eye") drawings, perspective drawings, and words using "cubes" as the unit of measure.	• Students who find the "top view" hard to visualize can be encouraged to use perspective-drawing to record their prisms.

Preparation and Planning

Pacing	**5–10 min** Introduction **15–25 min** Teaching and Learning **20–25 min** Consolidation
Materials	• set of linking cubes/group • (optional) a variety of rectangle-based prisms, including some cubes (square-based prism) • (optional) string
Masters	• Mental Math, p. 64
Workbook	p. 102, all questions
Vocabulary/ Symbols	volume, modelling, length, width, height
Key Assessment of Learning Question	Question 5, Application of Procedures

Meeting Individual Needs

Extra Challenge

- Students could collect containers that are not rectangle-based prisms (such as cylinders, other containers with curved surfaces, and containers made of two regular 3-D shapes), and model the approximate volume of these containers using cubes.
- Students could use centimetre cubes to model the volume of a variety of containers, to develop a sense of volume in cubic centimetres (cm^3).

Extra Support

- If students find it difficult to record their prisms using either "top view" drawings or perspective drawings, they could be encouraged to draw the 2-D "layers" of their prisms, which is not as demanding visually or artistically.

1. Introduction (Whole Class)
▶ 5–10 min

Show students a piece of string and explain that it is a 1-dimensional (1-D) object because it has just 1 dimension to measure, length. (Note: In reality, the string has length, width, and height but students can visualize it as linear with 1 dimension.) Explain that a surface such as a desktop, wall, or chalkboard has 2 dimensions (2-D), length and width. Explain that you can measure the area of a surface such as a desk by covering the surface with square centimetres or related square measures.

Draw attention to the vocabulary box on Student Book page 310. Hold up the Student Book and explain that the *volume* of the text is an attribute of a 3-D object and a measure of the space it occupies. A 3-D object has length, width, and height. Tell students they will be estimating the volume of rectangle-based and square-based prisms using linking cubes.

Sample Discourse

"What units would you use to record the length of this string?"
- *Centimetres or metres.*

"How is the top of your desk different from a piece of string? Does it have only a length, like the string?"
- *A desk has length and width.*

"What are some 3-dimensional (3-D) objects you can find in our classroom?"
- *A chalk brush, pens, chairs, and books*

"How is measuring the chalk brush different from measuring a desk top?"
- *It has 3 dimensions: length, width, and height.*

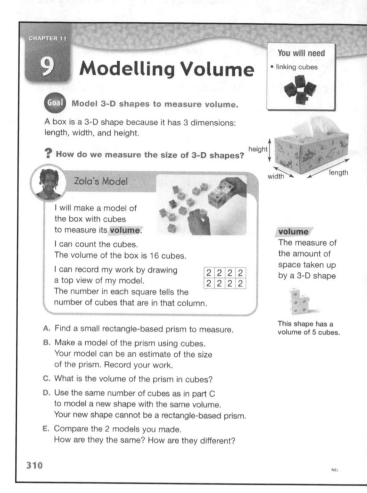

2. Teaching and Learning (Whole Class/Small Group) ▶ 15–25 min

Read together the central question and Zola's Model. Have students build Zola's model, then point out that this model is represented by the drawing on page 310 showing that each column has two cubes. Repeat with other models of rectangle-based prisms.

Distribute rectangle-based prisms and cubes to small groups, and tell students they are going to answer the central question by answering prompts A to E. Ask them to model their prisms using the cubes, record the models the same way Zola did, and count the total number of cubes to determine the volume. Have each group share their prism, the number of cubes in each row and column, and the total volume with the class. For prompts D and E, ensure that students understand that the total number of cubes determines the volume, not the shape of the object. The same number of cubes can be used to make different shapes with the same volume.

Reflecting

Use these questions to allow students the opportunity to apply what they have learned about determining the volume of a 3-D shape by finding the total number of cubes. Discuss the questions and encourage a variety of responses and examples.

Sample Discourse

1. • *The volume stays the same, because you aren't changing the number of cubes in the shape.*
   • *You aren't changing the shape. Instead you are looking at it from different directions, so the number of cubes doesn't change.*

2. • *They are different volumes because the cubes are different sizes.*

3. • *You can't know which shape it will be, because the same number of cubes could be arranged in lots of different ways, but still with the same volume.*

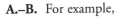

Reflecting

1. If you turn a 3-D shape upside down or sideways, does its volume change? Give a reason for your answer.

2. Zola created these 2 prisms. Both prisms use the same number of cubes. Do they have the same volume? Explain.

3. If you know only the volume of a 3-D shape, can you describe its shape? Explain.

Checking

4. a) Find a square-based prism. Estimate its volume by making a model with cubes. Record your work.

   b) Use the same cubes to model 2 other shapes with the same volume. Make one a rectangle-based prism and the other a different shape. Record your work for both shapes.

Practising

5. Build each shape. What is the volume of each shape?

a)   b)   c)

6. Make 2 different prisms with each volume. Record your work.

   a) 18 cubes   b) 30 cubes

7. Create a model of a 3-D shape using cubes. Record your work. Describe your model using measurement and geometry words.

— **Key Assessment of Learning question. (See chart on next page.)**

Answers

A.–B. For example,

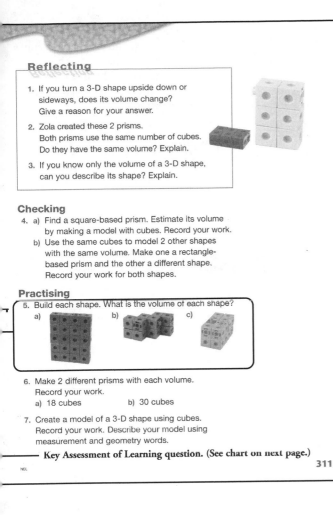

2	2	2
2	2	2
2	2	2

or

3	3	3
3	3	3

C. For example, the volume is 18 cubes.

D. For example,

or

E. For example, they are both 3-D models using the same number of cubes. They are different in that one shape is a rectangle-based prism and one is not and the shapes have different numbers of faces and vertices.

1. No, because there are the same number of cubes in the 3-D shape no matter how you hold it

2. No, because the yellow cubes are larger than the orange cubes.

---

3. Consolidation ▸ 20–25 min

Checking (Pairs)

For intervention strategies, refer to the Meeting Individual Needs box or the Assessment for Feedback chart.

Remind students what square-based and rectangle-based prisms are. Monitor to ensure that both partners do some recording and building.

Practising (Individual)

Here students work individually to consolidate their understanding of volume, using linking cubes.

5. b) & c) Although not all the cubes are visible, most students will assume they are meant to include them in their models. However, since they can't be seen, it is also correct to build these models with the "hidden" cubes missing as long as the model holds together. For example, if students assume there are one or more missing cubes, then the answers for **b)** could also be 10 or 11, and for **c)** 13, 14, or 15.

Closing (Whole Class)

Have students summarize their learning by asking, "Describe the process for modelling the volume of a 3-D shape."

* *I looked at my prism, and then I matched one face with linking cubes. It didn't work out exactly, but it was okay because we were* estimating *the volume, so it doesn't have to be exact. Then when I had one face done, I added another face, and then filled in all the others to make a prism. When my prism was finished I counted all the cubes, and that number was the volume of my prism.*

3. No, because many different 3-D shapes can have the same volume.

4. a) For example,

2	2	2
2	2	2
2	2	2

   b) For example,

3	3	3
3	3	3

and

5. a) 20 cubes

   b) 12 cubes

   c) 16 cubes

6. a) For example,

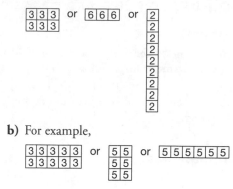

b) For example,

| 3 | 3 | 3 | 3 | 3 |
| 3 | 3 | 3 | 3 | 3 |

or

5	5
5	5
5	5

or

| 5 | 5 | 5 | 5 | 5 | 5 |

7. For example, I made a rectangle-based prism with a length of 4 cubes, width of 3 cubes, and height of 2 cubes. The prism's volume is 24 cubes. The base and the top faces are 4 cube by 3 cube rectangles. The front and back faces are 4 cube by 2 cube rectangles and the two end faces are 3 cubes by 2 cubes rectangles.

2	2	2	2
2	2	2	2
2	2	2	2

Assessment of Learning—What to Look for in Student Work...

Assessment Strategy: short answer
Application of Procedures

Key Assessment Question 5
• Build each shape. What is the volume of each shape?
  (Score 1 point for each correct shape and 1 point for each correct volume, for a total of 6.)

Extra Practice and Extension

• You might assign any of the questions related to this lesson, which are cross-referenced in the chart below.

Skills Bank	Student Book p. 313, Questions 10 & 11
Chapter Review	Student Book p. 317, Question 10
Workbook	p. 102, all questions
Nelson Web Site	Visit **www.mathk8.nelson.com** and follow the links to *Nelson Mathematics 4*, Chapter 11.

At Home

• Students could take home some linking cubes, and find the volume of a variety of prisms at home. The kitchen is a good source of prisms, because food is often packaged in prisms. They could also try estimating the volume of empty cans, using centimetre cubes.

Math Background

Although students will later learn the formula for finding volume, that is not required at this level. However, to prepare students for learning the formula, it is a good idea to always present the dimensions in the same order: length, followed by width, followed by height. Some students may observe that these dimensions may seem to "change" when the 3-D object is viewed from different perspectives (i.e., when the object is rotated the length and width are reversed). Point out, or have them discover, that the volume remains constant when the viewing perspective changes, because the actual dimensions of the object don't change, just the perspective. This provides a good context for teaching the commutative nature of multiplication, which states that the order of the factors doesn't change the product.

Skills Bank

Using the Skills Bank

Materials: balance scales, food items (showing mass and capacity), empty containers, linking cubes

1. Some students will benefit from having these shapes available to look at rather than only looking at them in the text. Remind students that **b)** and **c)** refer to the *sides* of faces.

4. Refer students to Lesson 4 to review how to draw 3-D shapes. Suggest they use the same techniques to answer this question.

5. & 6. Have boxes and containers available for students to help them with their estimations. The List of Food and Clothing List Master from Lesson 6 will also be a useful reference.

10. & 11. Distribute linking cubes to assist students with these answers.

Answers

1. a) B, C, D
   b) A, C
   c) A, B, C, D

2. a) A, C
   b) B, D

3. a) D
   b) A, B, C, D

4. a)

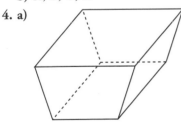

   b)

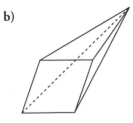

5. For example,
   a) sugar cube
   b) small candy bar
   c) large chocolate bar
   d) bag of sugar or flour
   e) backpack full of clothes
   f) an adult

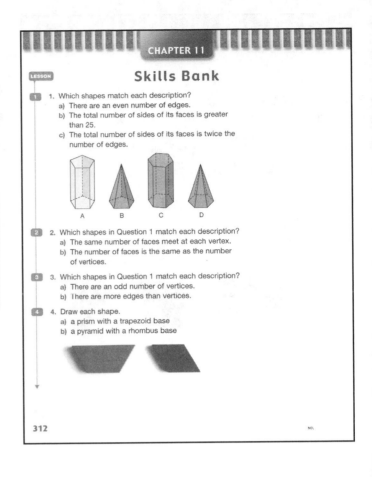

LESSON

1 **1.** Which shapes match each description?
   a) There are an even number of edges.
   b) The total number of sides of its faces is greater than 25.
   c) The total number of sides of its faces is twice the number of edges.

     A   B   C   D

2 **2.** Which shapes in Question 1 match each description?
   a) The same number of faces meet at each vertex.
   b) The number of faces is the same as the number of vertices.

3 **3.** Which shapes in Question 1 match each description?
   a) There are an odd number of vertices.
   b) There are more edges than vertices.

4 **4.** Draw each shape.
   a) a prism with a trapezoid base
   b) a pyramid with a rhombus base

312

NEL

6. For example,
   a) a small spoon
   b) an aquarium
   c) gas tank of a big car
   d) bottle of liquid glue
   e) a small juice glass
   f) an average-sized water bottle

7. a) litres
   b) millilitres
   c) millilitres
   d) millilitres
   e) litres
   f) litres

8. a) grams
   b) kilograms
   c) grams
   d) kilograms
   e) grams
   f) kilograms

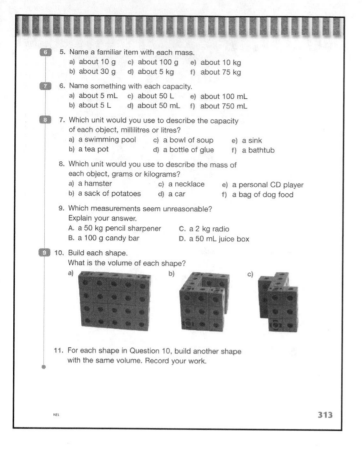

5. Name a familiar item with each mass.
  a) about 10 g   c) about 100 g   e) about 10 kg
  b) about 30 g   d) about 5 kg   f) about 75 kg

6. Name something with each capacity.
  a) about 5 mL   c) about 50 L   e) about 100 mL
  b) about 5 L   d) about 50 mL   f) about 750 mL

7. Which unit would you use to describe the capacity of each object, millilitres or litres?
  a) a swimming pool   c) a bowl of soup   e) a sink
  b) a tea pot   d) a bottle of glue f) a bathtub

8. Which unit would you use to describe the mass of each object, grams or kilograms?
  a) a hamster   c) a necklace   e) a personal CD player
  b) a sack of potatoes d) a car   f) a bag of dog food

9. Which measurements seem unreasonable? Explain your answer.
  A. a 50 kg pencil sharpener   C. a 2 kg radio
  B. a 100 g candy bar   D. a 50 mL juice box

10. Build each shape. What is the volume of each shape?
  a)   b)   c)

11. For each shape in Question 10, build another shape with the same volume. Record your work.

9. For example,
  A. unreasonable — because this is more than the mass of a student
  D. unreasonable — because even small juice boxes are about 200 mL

10. a) 20 cubes

b) 24 cubes

c) 18 cubes

11. a) 20 cubes

| 2 | 2 | 2 | 2 | 2 | 2 | 2 | 2 | 2 | 2 |

or

2	2
2	2
2	2
2	2
2	2

b) 24 cubes

| 2 | 2 | 2 | 2 | 2 | 2 | 2 | 2 | 2 | 2 | 2 | 2 |

or

3	3	3	3
3	3	3	3

or

6	6
6	6

c) 18 cubes

| 2 | 2 | 2 | 2 | 2 | 2 | 2 | 2 | 2 |

or

| 3 | 3 | 3 | 3 | 3 | 3 |

or

6	6
6	

Problem Bank

Using the Problem Bank

Materials: triangle-based prism, toothpicks, modelling clay, square-based prism or blocks, 3-D solids, teaspoon, measuring cup

1. Students could model this question by making the prism with modelling clay.

2. Ask students to first consider whether this is a prism or a pyramid, given that 2 faces are different from the other 6.

3. Students could use toothpicks and modelling clay to help them with this question.

5. Remind students that toothpicks are just like edges in the model.

10. & 11. Prompt students by reminding them what similar measures (e.g., 250 mL in a measuring cup and 5 mL in a teaspoon) look like.

Answers

1. 11 faces; each cut adds 1 face (6 new faces) and there are 5 original faces (6 + 5 = 11)

2. a hexagon-based prism

3. a) For example, a tetrahedron (a triangle-based pyramid) or a cube

   b) For example, tetrahedron — 6 toothpicks; cube — 12 toothpicks

   c) For example, tetrahedron — 4 pieces of modelling clay; cube — 8 pieces of modelling clay

4. a) For example, 5 apples (4 in the bottom layer + 1), or 14 apples (9 in the bottom layer + 4 in the next layer + 1), or 30 apples (16 + 9 + 4 + 1), and so on

   b) Because you don't know the number of layers or the total number of apples

5. a triangle-based prism and a pentagon-based pyramid

6. 8 cartons (1 full carton = 625 g × 8 = 5000g = 5 kg)

7. red bag: cereal, apple, and bread; or, bread and cereal

   green bag: apple or cereal

   yellow bag: apple and bread

8. $100; $100 in pennies is about 25 kg, $1000 in pennies is about 250 kg.

9. Greater because each wiener has a mass of 45 g and each bun has a mass of about the same, so that is more than 50 g.

10. No, you would need a larger pitcher since 4 × 350 mL is more than 1 L (1000 mL)

11. a) 4 mL/minute

    b) 4 mL/min × 60 = 240 mL/hour

    c) 240 mL × 24 h = 5760 mL, about 6 L

    d) about 6 kg

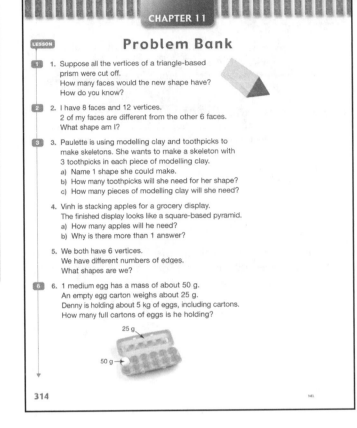

Problem Bank

LESSON

1. 1. Suppose all the vertices of a triangle-based prism were cut off.
How many faces would the new shape have? How do you know?

2. 2. I have 8 faces and 12 vertices.
2 of my faces are different from the other 6 faces.
What shape am I?

3. 3. Paulette is using modelling clay and toothpicks to make skeletons. She wants to make a skeleton with 3 toothpicks in each piece of modelling clay.
a) Name 1 shape she could make.
b) How many toothpicks will she need for her shape?
c) How many pieces of modelling clay will she need?

4. Vinh is stacking apples for a grocery display.
The finished display looks like a square-based pyramid.
a) How many apples will he need?
b) Why is there more than 1 answer?

5. We both have 6 vertices.
We have different numbers of edges.
What shapes are we?

6. 6. 1 medium egg has a mass of about 50 g.
An empty egg carton weighs about 25 g.
Denny is holding about 5 kg of eggs, including cartons.
How many full cartons of eggs is he holding?

314

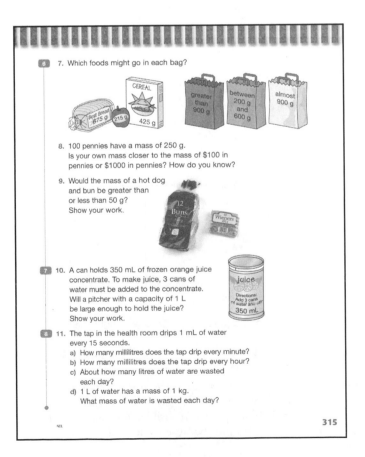

6. 7. Which foods might go in each bag?

8. 100 pennies have a mass of 250 g.
Is your own mass closer to the mass of $100 in pennies or $1000 in pennies? How do you know?

9. Would the mass of a hot dog and bun be greater than or less than 50 g? Show your work.

7. 10. A can holds 350 mL of frozen orange juice concentrate. To make juice, 3 cans of water must be added to the concentrate. Will a pitcher with a capacity of 1 L be large enough to hold the juice? Show your work.

8. 11. The tap in the health room drips 1 mL of water every 15 seconds.
a) How many millilitres does the tap drip every minute?
b) How many millilitres does the tap drip every hour?
c) About how many litres of water are wasted each day?
d) 1 L of water has a mass of 1 kg.
What mass of water is wasted each day?

315

Chapter Review

Using the Chapter Review

Use these pages to assess students' understanding of the concepts developed in the chapter. Refer to the assessment chart on the next page for the details of each question.

Preparation and Planning

Materials	variety of prisms and pyramids, toothpicks and modelling clay (or straws and tape)
Workbook	p. 103, all questions
Masters	Chapter 11 Test Pages 1 & 2, pp. 65–66

Journal

Ask students to record in their journals their thoughts now, having completed the chapter, about the chapter goal that they wrote about at the beginning of the chapter. (See Chapter 11 Opener Teacher's Resource page 9.) Then have them compare their responses and reflect on what they have learned.

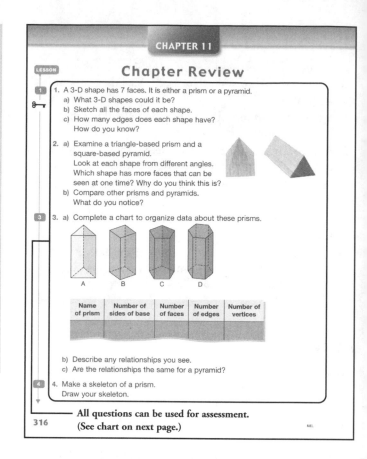

Answers

1. a) a hexagon-based pyramid or a pentagon-based prism

b)

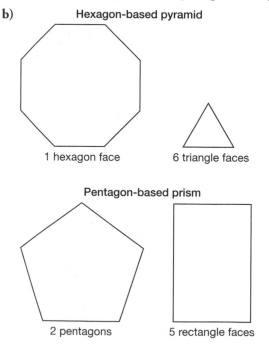

Hexagon-based pyramid

1 hexagon face   6 triangle faces

Pentagon-based prism

2 pentagons   5 rectangle faces

c) hexagon-based pyramid: 12 edges; pentagon-based prism: 15 edges

2. a) Square-based pyramids have more faces visible at one time (4 faces out of 5); only 3 of the 5 faces of the triangle-based prism are visible. You can see more faces on pyramids because some are slanted.

b) For a pyramid you can always see 1 less than the total number of faces; for a prism there are always 2 or more faces hidden.

3. a)

Name of Prism	Number of sides of base	Number of faces	Number of edges	Number of vertices
A. triangle-based prism	3	5	9	6
B. square-based prism	4	6	12	8
C. pentagon-based prism	5	7	15	10
D. hexagon-based prism	6	8	18	12

b) For example, there are always more edges than faces or vertices; there are always more vertices than faces; as the number of sides of the base increases by 1, the number of faces increases by 1, edges increase by 3, and vertices increase by 2.

c) Similar relationships: there are always more edges than faces or vertices; there are always more vertices than faces. Dissimilar relationships: the relationship between the number of sides of base and faces, edges and vertices. In a pyramid, as you increase the number of sides of the base by 1, you increase the number of faces by 1, edges by 1, and vertices by 1.

4. Students' sketches will vary. Refer to previous sketches in this Teacher's Resource or in the Student Book for any prism.

5. For example, there are 5 congruent triangles that meet at the top vertex. The base is a pentagon. Each side of the base pentagon forms an edge with one of the triangles.

6. a) Yes

b) For example, she is close enough and has prepared an order that is not more than the customer asked for. One slice probably has a mass greater than 2 g, so she cannot get closer while staying under the request.

7. A. is 50 g less

B. is 20 g more

C. is 410 g less

8. For example,

a) about 250 mL

b) about 500 mL

c) about 900 mL

d) about 200 mL

9. a) kilograms

b) kilograms

c) grams

d) millilitres

e) litres

f) millilitres

10. a)

b) 9 cubes

c) For example,

The volume is 9 cubes.

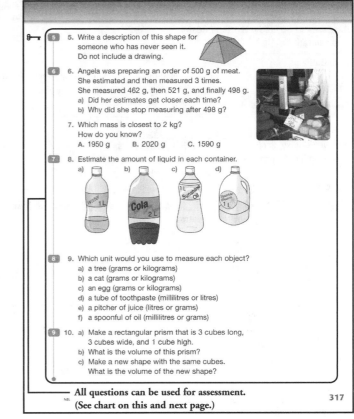

5. Write a description of this shape for someone who has never seen it. Do not include a drawing.

6. Angela was preparing an order of 500 g of meat. She estimated and then measured 3 times. She measured 462 g, then 521 g, and finally 498 g.
a) Did her estimates get closer each time?
b) Why did she stop measuring after 498 g?

7. Which mass is closest to 2 kg? How do you know?
A. 1950 g   B. 2020 g   C. 1590 g

8. Estimate the amount of liquid in each container.
a)   b)   c)   d)

9. Which unit would you use to measure each object?
a) a tree (grams or kilograms)
b) a cat (grams or kilograms)
c) an egg (grams or kilograms)
d) a tube of toothpaste (millilitres or litres)
e) a pitcher of juice (litres or grams)
f) a spoonful of oil (millilitres or grams)

10. a) Make a rectangular prism that is 3 cubes long, 3 cubes wide, and 1 cube high.
b) What is the volume of this prism?
c) Make a new shape with the same cubes. What is the volume of the new shape?

All questions can be used for assessment. (See chart on this and next page.)

NEL   317

Assessment of Learning—What to Look for in Student Work...

Assessment Strategy: written question
Problem Solving

Question 1
- A 3-D shape has 7 faces. It is either a prism or a pyramid.
 a) What 3-D shapes could it be?
 b) Sketch all the faces of each shape.
 c) How many edges does each shape have? How do you know?

1	2	3	4
Carry Out the Plan			
• uses a strategy and attempts to determine the 3-D shapes but does not arrive at an answer • makes major errors and/or omissions when sketching faces and determining the number of edges	• carries out a plan to some extent, using a strategy, and develops a partial and/or incorrect solution • makes several errors and/or omissions when sketching faces and determining the number of edges	• carries out a plan effectively by using an appropriate strategy to determine the possible 3-D shapes • makes a few minor errors and/or omissions when sketching faces and determining the number of edges	• shows flexibility and insight by trying and adapting one or more strategies to determine the possible 3-D shapes • makes almost no errors when sketching faces and determining the number of edges
Communicate			
• provides an incomplete explanation of thinking	• provides a partial explanation of thinking	• provides a complete and clear explanation of thinking	• provides a thorough, clear, and insightful explanation of thinking

Assessment of Learning—What to Look for in Student Work...

Assessment Strategy: written question
Communication

Question 2
a) Examine a triangle-based prism and a square-based pyramid. Look at each shape from different angles.
   Which shape has more faces that can be seen at one time? Why do you think this is?
b) Compare other prisms and pyramids. What do you notice?

1	2	3	4
• provides an incomplete or inaccurate explanation of geometric properties and relationships, using very little mathematical language	• provides a partial explanation of geometric properties and relationships, using some mathematical language correctly	• provides a complete and clear explanation of geometric properties and relationships, using mathematical language correctly	• provides a thorough and clear explanation of geometric properties and relationships, using precise mathematical language

Assessment Strategy: written question
Application of Procedures, Understanding of Concepts

Question 3
a) Complete a chart to organize data about these prisms.
b) Describe any relationships you see.
c) Are the relationships the same for a pyramid?

1	2	3	4
Application of Procedures			
• makes major errors and/or omissions when completing the chart	• makes several errors and/or omissions when completing the chart	• makes only a few minor errors when completing the chart	• makes almost no errors when completing the chart
Understanding of Concepts			
• uses the information in the chart to make very simple observations about the geometric relationships of prisms and pyramids	• uses the information in the chart to make simple observations about the geometric relationships of prisms and pyramids	• uses the information in the chart to make grade-appropriate observations about the geometric relationships of prisms and pyramids	• uses the information in the chart to make insightful observations about the geometric relationships of prisms and pyramids

Assessment Strategy: written question
Application of Procedures

Question 4
• Make a skeleton of a prism. Draw your skeleton.

1	2	3	4
• makes major errors and/or omissions when making and drawing a skeleton of a prism	• makes several errors and/or omissions when making and drawing a skeleton of a prism	• makes only a few errors when making and drawing a skeleton of a prism	• makes almost no errors when making and drawing a skeleton of a prism

Assessment Strategy: written question
Communication

Question 5
• Write a description of this shape for someone who has never seen it. Do not include a drawing.

1	2	3	4
• provides an incomplete or inaccurate description of the shape	• provides a partial description of the shape that exhibits some clarity and thought	• provides a complete and clear description of the shape	• provides a thorough, clear, and insightful description of the shape
• uses very little mathematical language correctly	• uses some mathematical language correctly	• uses mathematical language correctly	• uses precise mathematical language correctly

Assessment Strategy: written question
Problem Solving

Question 6
- Angela was preparing an order of 500 g of meat. She estimated and then measured 3 times. She measured 462 g, then 521 g, and finally 498 g.
  a) Did her estimates get closer each time?
  b) Why did she stop measuring after 498 g?

1	2	3	4
• provides an incomplete or inaccurate explanation of thinking	• provides a partial explanation of thinking	• provides a complete and clear explanation of thinking	• provides a thorough, clear, and insightful explanation of thinking

---

Assessment Strategy: short answer
Understanding of Concepts

Question 7
- Which mass is closest to 2 kg? How do you know?
  A. 1950 g
  B. 2020 g
  C. 1590 g
  (Score 1 point for correct response and 1 point for appropriate reason, for a total of 2.)

Assessment Strategy: short answer
Application of Procedures

Question 8
- Estimate the amount of liquid in each container.
(Score correct responses out of 4.)

Assessment Strategy: short answer
Understanding of Concepts

Question 9
- Which unit would you use to measure each object?
  a) a tree (grams or kilograms)
  b) a cat (grams or kilograms)
  c) an egg (grams or kilograms)
  d) a tube of toothpaste (millilitres or litres)
  e) a pitcher of juice (litres or grams)
  f) a spoonful of oil (millilitres or grams)
  (Score correct responses out of 6.)

Assessment Strategy: skills demonstration, short answer
Application of Procedures

Question 10
a) Make a rectangular prism that is 3 cubes long, 3 cubes wide, and 1 cube high.
b) What is the volume of this prism?
c) Make a new shape with the same cubes. What is the volume of the new shape?
(Score 1 point each for correct shapes and 1 point each for correct volumes, for a total of 4.)

Chapter Task

Expectations

4m50 use linear dimensions and perimeter [and area measures with precision] to measure length, perimeter, and area

4m57 model three-dimensional figures of specific volumes using blocks

4m59 select the most appropriate standard unit to measure mass

4m63 draw and build three-dimensional objects and models

4m78 recognize and describe the occurrence and application of geometric properties and principles in the everyday world

Use this task as an opportunity for performance assessment, to give you a sense of students' understanding of volume and mass and their ability to apply and communicate their understanding of geometry and measurement concepts to describe an object.

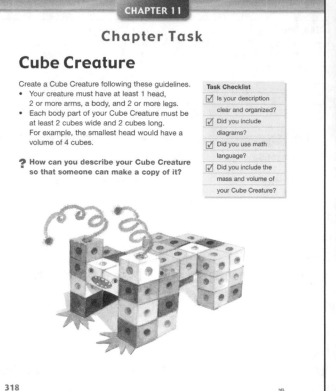

Preparation and Planning

Pacing	**10–15 min** Introducing the Chapter Task **30–45 min** Using the Chapter Task
Materials	• linking cubes • rulers • balance scales and masses
Masters	• 2 cm Grid Paper, Masters Booklet, p. 24 • Chapter 11 Task Pages 1 & 2, pp. 67–68
Enabling Activities	• Brainstorm geometry and measurement words to describe 3-D shapes (Chapter 11, Getting Started) • Communicate an understanding of geometric concepts (See Lesson 5.) • Estimate, measure, and record the mass objects (See Lesson 6.) • Create 3-D shapes using cubes, record and describe your model using measurement and geometry words (See Lesson 9, question 7.)
Nelson Web Site	• Visit **www.mathk8.nelson.com** and follow the links to *Nelson Mathematics 4*, Chapter 11 to view samples of students' work and assessment support notes.

Introducing the Chapter Task
(Whole Class) ▶ 10–15 min

Look at the picture on page 318. Ask students why they think it is called a cube creature. Tell the students that they are going to create their own cube creature. Together read the guidelines for constructing a cube creatures. Inform students that wings can be substituted for arms and fins for legs.

Allow students 10 min for building their creatures. At the end of 10 min, remove all the unused linking cubes.

Using the Chapter Task
(Individual) ▶ 30–45 min

Together, review all the information provided on Student Book page 318. Point out that the Task Checklist at the right side of the page shows reminders about how to make an excellent solution. Some students may be able to work through the task as it is described on the student page; however, most students will benefit from using the 2 masters to plan and record their work. (If you want to consider a different performance assessment idea, see Adapting the Task on the next page.)

While students are working, observe and/or interview individuals to see how they are interpreting and carrying out the task. Observe how students measure the mass of their creature. Competent students will estimate first by beginning with the largest masses and then adding smaller and smaller masses. Students who require more opportunities will randomly add masses, often starting with the smallest masses, adding the larger masses when they run out of small masses.

Assessing Students' Work

Use this chart as a guide for assessing students' work. To view samples of students' work at different levels, visit the Nelson Web site **www.mathk8.nelson.com.**

Assessment of Learning—What to Look for in Student Work...

Assessment Strategy: observation and product marking
Problem Solving

	1	2	3	4
Communication Explanation and justification of mathematical concepts, procedures, and problem solving	• provides incomplete or inaccurate explanations/ justifications of mass and volume that lack clarity or logical thought, using minimal words, pictures, symbols, and/or numbers	• provides partial explanations/justifications of mass and volume that exhibit some clarity and logical thought, using simple words, pictures, symbols, and/or numbers	• provides complete, clear, and logical explanations/ justifications of mass and volume, using appropriate words, pictures, symbols, and/or numbers	• provides thorough, clear, and insightful explanations/ justifications of mass and volume, using a range of words, pictures, symbols, and/or numbers
Communication Organization of material (written, spoken, or drawn)	• organization of creature description is minimal and seriously impedes communication	• organization of creature description is limited but does not seriously impede communication	• organization of creature description is sufficient to support communication	• organization of creature description is effective and aids communication
Communication Use of mathematical vocabulary	• uses very little mathematical vocabulary to describe linear measurements and geometric attributes, and vocabulary used lacks clarity and precision	• uses a limited range of mathematical vocabulary with some degree of clarity and precision to describe linear measurements and geometric attributes	• uses mathematical vocabulary with sufficient clarity and precision to describe linear measurements and geometric attributes	• uses a broad range of mathematical vocabulary to clearly and precisely describe linear measurements and geometric attributes
Communication Use of mathematical conventions (e.g., grams, cubes, units, angle measures, labels)	• few conventions are used correctly	• some conventions are used correctly	• most conventions are used correctly	• almost all conventions are used correctly

Adapting the Task

You can adapt the task in the student book to suit the needs of your students. For example:

*   Use the masters for Chapter 11 Task Pages 1 & 2, pp. 67–68.
*   Spread the task over 2 days to allow for greater exploration and design of Cube Creatures.
*   Do a similar task in small groups first if the master is not used in order to scaffold and consolidate the concepts in the chapter. For example, create a toy using the linking cubes for a small toddler and describe it using geometry and measurement words. Examine student work, compiling a chart listing the different ways each group described their toy and discuss/evaluate the various formats used to communicate this information. This also allows you to assess their ability to work cooperatively in small groups.
*   If you have a limited number of balances you may wish to set up a centre and have students take turns going to the centre and measuring the mass of their creature throughout the day.

Cumulative Review

Using the Cumulative Review

Masters: 1 cm Grid Paper, Masters Booklet p. 23

The questions on Student Book page 319 provide practice with multiple-choice questions, while reviewing the concepts developed in Chapters 8 to 11.

The questions on Student Book page 320 offer an investigation that can be used to assess students' understanding. Refer to the assessment chart on the next page for the details of each question.

Question	Chapter	ON Expectations
1	8	4m49
2	9	4m25
3	10	4m30
4	11	4m68
5	11	4m56
6	11	4m59
7. a)	9	4m7
7. b)	10	4m7
8. a)	8	4m36, 4m51
8. b)	8	4m52
9	11	4m77, 4m78

Answers

1. A
2. F
3. B
4. H
5. A
6. F
7. a) For example,

$$8 \times 7 = 56 \text{ and } 5 \times 80 = 400$$

   b) 76

8. a) Yes. The sidewalk has an area of 20 m² and the field also has an area of 20 m². So, 40 m² for walking and running. The swings and slide have an area of 4 m², the sandbox also has an area of 4 m², the climbers have an area of 12 m². So, 20 m² for playing on equipment.

   b) The sidewalk and the field are the same because they each are shown by 20 squares. As well, the swings/slide and sandbox are the same because they each are shown by 4 squares.

9. 2-dimensional: squares, rectangles, trapezoids; 3-dimensional: cube, square-based pyramid, triangle-based prism, square-based prism.

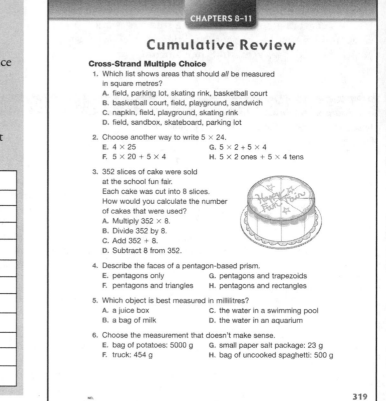

CHAPTERS 8–11

Cumulative Review

Cross-Strand Multiple Choice

1. Which list shows areas that should *all* be measured in square metres?
   A. field, parking lot, skating rink, basketball court
   B. basketball court, field, playground, sandwich
   C. napkin, field, playground, skating rink
   D. field, sandbox, skateboard, parking lot

2. Choose another way to write 5 × 24.
   E. 4 × 25
   F. 5 × 20 + 5 × 4
   G. 5 × 2 + 5 × 4
   H. 5 × 2 ones + 5 × 4 tens

3. 352 slices of cake were sold at the school fun fair. Each cake was cut into 8 slices. How would you calculate the number of cakes that were used?
   A. Multiply 352 × 8.
   B. Divide 352 by 8.
   C. Add 352 + 8.
   D. Subtract 8 from 352.

4. Describe the faces of a pentagon-based prism.
   E. pentagons only
   F. pentagons and triangles
   G. pentagons and trapezoids
   H. pentagons and rectangles

5. Which object is best measured in millilitres?
   A. a juice box
   B. a bag of milk
   C. the water in a swimming pool
   D. the water in an aquarium

6. Choose the measurement that doesn't make sense.
   E. bag of potatoes: 5000 g
   F. truck: 454 g
   G. small paper salt package: 23 g
   H. bag of uncooked spaghetti: 500 g

319

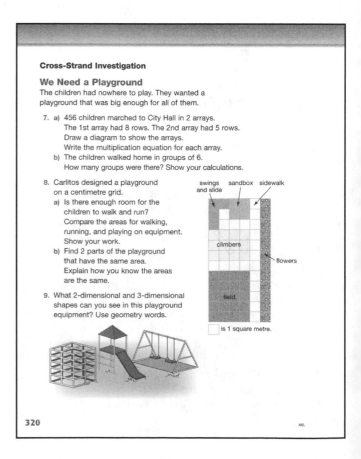

Cross-Strand Investigation

We Need a Playground
The children had nowhere to play. They wanted a playground that was big enough for all of them.

7. a) 456 children marched to City Hall in 2 arrays. The 1st array had 8 rows. The 2nd array had 5 rows. Draw a diagram to show the arrays. Write the multiplication equation for each array.
   b) The children walked home in groups of 6. How many groups were there? Show your calculations.

8. Carlitos designed a playground on a centimetre grid.
   a) Is there enough room for the children to walk and run? Compare the areas for walking, running, and playing on equipment. Show your work.
   b) Find 2 parts of the playground that have the same area. Explain how you know the areas are the same.

9. What 2-dimensional and 3-dimensional shapes can you see in this playground equipment? Use geometry words.

swings and slide   sandbox   sidewalk

climbers

flowers

field

☐ is 1 square metre.

320

Assessment of Learning—What to Look for in Student Work...

Assessment Strategy: written question
Problem Solving

Question 7
- The children had nowhere to play. They wanted a playground that was big enough for all of them.
  a) 456 children marched to City Hall in 2 arrays. The 1st array had 8 rows. The 2nd array had 5 rows. Draw a diagram to show the arrays. Write the multiplication equation for each array.
  b) The children walked home in groups of 6. How many groups were there? Show your calculations.

1	2	3	4
Carry Out the Plan			
• uses a strategy and attempts to solve the problem, but is unable to draw arrays	• carries out a plan to some extent, using a strategy, and draws partial and/or incorrect arrays	• carries out a plan effectively by using an appropriate strategy to draw the arrays	• shows flexibility and insight when carrying out a plan by trying and adapting one or more strategies to draw the arrays
• makes major errors and/or omissions when writing multiplication equations for each array and when calculating the number of groups	• makes several errors and/or omissions when writing multiplication equations for each array and when calculating the number of groups	• makes a few minor errors when writing multiplication equations for each array and when calculating the number of groups	• makes almost no errors when writing multiplication equations for each array and when calculating the number of groups

Assessment Strategy: written question
Application of Procedures

Question 8a
- Carlitos designed a playground on a centimetre grid.
  a) Is there enough room for the children to walk and run? Compare the areas for walking, running, and playing on equipment. Show your work.

1	2	3	4
• selects an inappropriate procedure to compare the areas	• selects a partially appropriate procedure to compare the areas	• selects an appropriate procedure to compare the areas	• selects the most efficient procedure to compare the areas
• makes major errors and/or omissions when applying procedures	• makes several errors and/or omissions when applying procedures	• makes only a few minor errors and/or omissions when applying procedures	• makes almost no errors when applying procedures

Assessment Strategy: written question
Understanding of Concepts

Question 8b
- **b)** Find 2 parts of the playground that have the same area. Explain how you know the areas are the same.

1	2	3	4
• demonstrates a superficial or inaccurate understanding that different 2-dimensional shapes can have the same area	• demonstrates a growing but still incomplete understanding that different 2-dimensional shapes can have the same area	• demonstrates grade-appropriate understanding that different 2-dimensional shapes can have the same area	• demonstrates in-depth understanding that different 2-dimensional shapes can have the same area

Assessment Strategy: written question
Communication

Question 9
- What 2-dimensional and 3-dimensional shapes can you see in this playground equipment? Use geometry words.

1	2	3	4
• provides incomplete or inaccurate descriptions that lack clarity or logical thought	• provides partial descriptions that exhibit some clarity and logical thought	• provides complete, clear, and logical descriptions of information shown in the graph	• provides thorough, clear, and insightful descriptions of shapes
• uses very little mathematical language and language used lacks clarity and precision	• uses a limited range of mathematical language with some degree of clarity and precision	• uses mathematical language with sufficient clarity and precision to communicate ideas	• uses a broad range of mathematical language to communicate clearly and precisely

Family Newsletter

Dear Parent/Caregiver:

In our next unit in mathematics, "3-D Geometry and 3-D Measurement," the students will be examining shapes and solids commonly seen around them. Over the next three weeks, your child will be learning to identify, build, and describe 3-D shapes.

Students will also be exploring connections between 3-D geometry and 3-D measurement. They will have many opportunities to estimate, measure, and compare the capacity, mass, and volume of the 3-D shapes with which they will be working.

Throughout this time, you and your child can practise some activities such as the following:

- Your child can find a box and show your family how many faces and edges it has.
- Your child can draw and label some items at home that are made up of 2-D shapes.
- Your child can name and sketch any object in your house that is made by combining 3-D shapes; for example, a sofa or bookshelf.
- Your child can find 3-D objects, measure them in different ways, and record their measurements and observations. For example, a chewy oatmeal bar is shaped like a rectangle-based prism. It measures 7 cm by 2 cm. It has a mass of 26 g. Find two more items: one with a mass less than the bar and one with a mass more than the bar.
- Your child can look at one box or container in your food cupboard. Together, write then answer questions about the box concerning geometry and measurement (mass, capacity) using any of the numerical data on the container. For example: a cake box— What shape is the package? (rectangle-based prism) What shape are the faces of the package? (rectangles) What are its dimensions? (use a ruler) How much water is needed to make the batter for one cake? How much oil? What is the mass of the package?

You may also want to visit the Nelson Web site at **www.mathk8.nelson.com** for more suggestions to help your child learn mathematics and for books that relate children's literature to 3-D geometry and/or 3-D measurement. Also check the Web site for links to other Web sites that provide online tutorials, math problems, and brainteasers.

If your child is using the *Nelson Mathematics 4 Workbook*, pages 94 to 103 belong to Chapter 11. There is a page of practice questions for each of the 9 lessons in the chapter and a Test Yourself page at the end. If your child requires assistance, you can refer to the At-Home Help section on each Workbook page.

Chapter 11: Mental Math Page 1

LESSON

1 **1.** Use mental math to find the next 3 numbers in each pattern.

    a) 9, 18, 27, _____, _____, _____

    b) 25, 50, 75, _____, _____, _____

    c) 50, 45, 40, _____, _____, _____

    d) 63, 54, 45, _____, _____, _____

    e) 2, 4, 8, _____, _____, _____

    f) 64, 32, 16, _____, _____, _____

2 **2.** This rectangle-based prism has 6 faces. Use mental math to find the perimeter of each face below.

    a) Face A

    b) Face B

    c) Face C

3. This rectangle-based prism has 6 faces. Use mental math to find the area of each of these 3 faces.

    a) Face A

    b) Face B

    c) Face C

    d) What is the total area of Faces A, B, and C?

    e) Use your answer to question **d)** to find the total area of all 6 faces of the rectangle-based prism.

4. This tent has a rectangular floor, 2 rectangular sides, and 2 triangular sides. Use mental math to find the perimeter of each side listed below.

    a) Side A

    b) Side B

    c) Side C

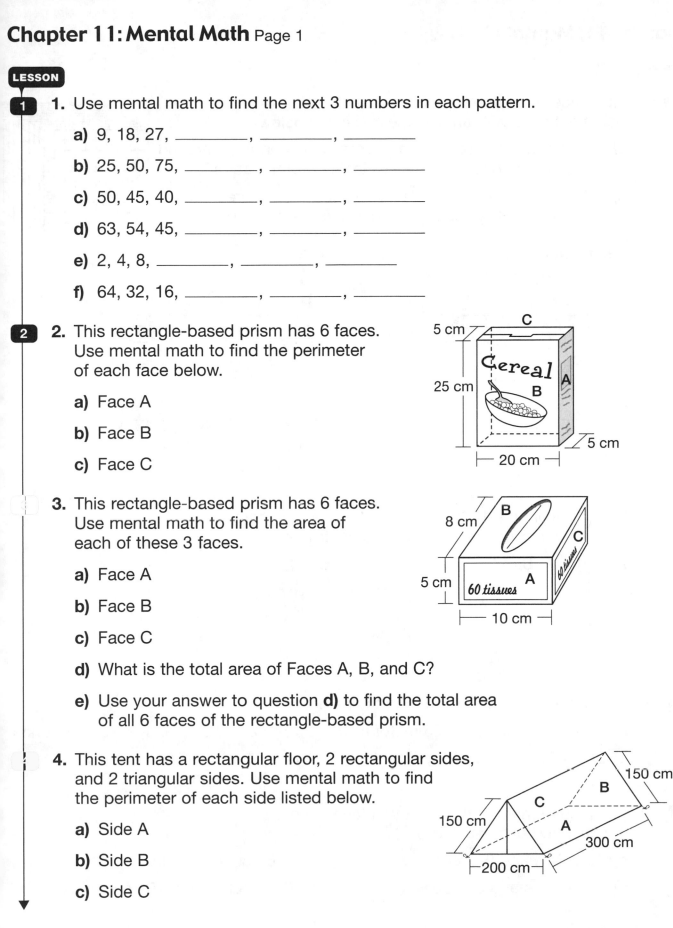

Chapter 11: Mental Math Page 2

LESSON

5 **5.** Each face of a cube is 10 cm by 10 cm.
Use mental math to answer the questions below.

   a) What is the area of
   1 face of the cube?

   b) What is the total area
   of 6 faces of the cube?

   c) What is the perimeter around
   each face of the cube?

   d) What is the total area of all
   of the faces on 3 cubes?

6. Use mental math to find the mass in grams
of the object with a ? mark.

a)

c)

b)

d)

7 **7.** Each container is 1 L or 1000 mL. Use mental math
to the amount needed to fill up the container.

   a)   **b)**   **c)**   **d)**

   500 mL   250 mL   925 mL   898 mL

8 **8.** Use mental math to the find the total amount.

   a) 175 mL of milk and 225 mL of milk

   b) 25 g of butter and 75 g of butter

   c) 100 g, 250 g, and 150 g of almonds

   d) 150 mL, 150 mL, and 250 mL of
   chicken broth

9 **9.** Use mental math to the find the total number
of cubes to build each solid.

   a) 18 cubes and 9 cubes

   b) 125 cubes and 50 cubes

   c) 64 cubes and 36 cubes

   d) 99 cubes and 101 cubes

Chapter 11 Test Page 1

1. A 3-D shape has 5 faces. It is either a prism or a pyramid.

   (a) What 3-D shapes could it be?

   (b) Sketch all of the faces of each shape.

   (c) How many edges does each shape have?

2. **(a)** I have 12 edges and 8 vertices. What shape am I?

   (b) I have 8 edges and 5 vertices. What shape am I?

3. How many straws or toothpicks do you need to make the skeleton of each shape?

   (a) a triangle-based pyramid

   (b) a triangle-based prism

   (c) a pentagon-based prism

   (d) a hexagon-based pyramid

4. Draw a square-based prism that looks 3-dimensional.

5. Write a description of this shape for someone who has never seen it.

Chapter 11 Test Page 2

6. You have a bag that will not hold more than 2 kg.
Make a list of the following items that you could fit into the bag.

loaf of bread—675 g   can of beans—680 g

orange—200 g   seeds and nuts—75 g

carton of eggs—350 g   1 L water—1 kg

apple—215 g   animal crackers—225 g

beef jerky—175 g   towel—378 g

T-shirt—62 g   sweatshirt—130 g

7. You are making a pot of soup. The can holds 250 mL of soup.
You open the can and pour the soup in a pot. Then, you must fill
the can twice with water and add it to the soup in the pot.
You have a choice of three pots: one with a capacity of 500 mL,
one with a capacity of 700 mL, and one with a capacity of 1 L.
Which pot should you make your soup in?

8. Which unit would you use to measure each object?

(a) a large container of cooking oil or pop (millilitres or litres)

(b) a can or drinking box with one serving of juice (millilitres or litres)

(c) a bowling ball (grams or kilograms)

(d) a tennis ball (grams or kilograms)

(e) a pencil (grams or kilograms)

(f) a spoonful of sugar (grams or millilitres)

9. If a rectangle-based prism is 5 cubes long, 3 cubes wide, and 2 cubes high,
what is the volume of this prism?

Chapter 11 Task Page 1

Cube Creature

STUDENT BOOK PAGE 318

Create a Cube Creature following these guidelines.

- Your creature must have at least 1 head, 2 or more arms, a body, and 2 or more legs.
- Each body part of your Cube Creature must be at least 2 cubes wide and 2 cubes long. For example, the smallest head would have a volume of 4 cubes.

Sketch your Cube Creature.

Answer the following questions about your Cube Creature.

How can you describe your Cube Creature so that someone can make a copy of it?

Chapter 11 Task Page 2

Cube Creature

STUDENT BOOK PAGE 318

What is the volume of your Cube Creature?

Show how you determined the volume.

Estimate the mass of your Cube Creature. Explain how you estimated.

Measure the mass of your Cube Creature.
How close was your measurement to your estimate?

How else can you describe your Cube Creature?
Think about linear dimensions and geometric attributes.

Name: _____ Date: _____

Scaffolding for Getting Started Activity
STUDENT BOOK PAGES 292–293

? **How can you describe the size and shapes of the packages?**

A. Examine 2 packages. Measure or estimate the packages to describe them.

	Package 1	**Package 2**
Size (large, medium, small)	_____	_____
Height (cm)	_____	_____
Width (cm)	_____	_____
Number of faces	_____	_____
Shapes of faces	_____	_____
Mass (g or kg)	_____	_____
Capacity (mL or L)	_____	_____

Look at the math words in the picture on page 292.

Math words that describe package 1:

_____

_____

Math words that describe package 2:

_____

_____

B. Examine the shape, size, number of edges, and number of faces.

What is 1 thing that is the same between your 2 packages?

_____

What is 1 thing that is different about your 2 packages?

_____

C. List 2 things that might come in each package.

Package 1 _____

Package 2 _____

D. Circle the words in your list that have to do with shape.
Underline the words that have to do with measuring.

Scaffolding for Do You Remember?

STUDENT BOOK PAGE 293

1. Draw a line to match each name with a shape.

   a) rectangle-based prism

   b) triangle-based prism

   c) triangle-based pyramid

   d) cone

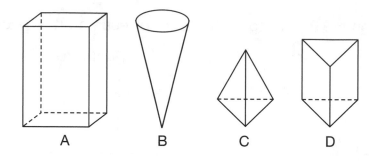

   A   B   C   D

2. Circle the shapes above that have congruent bases.

3. Count the number of faces, edges, and vertices and fill in the chart.

3-D shape	Number of faces	Number of edges	Number of vertices
_____ prism			
_____ pyramid			

4. Which is larger: a gram or a kilogram? _____

   Would you use grams or kilograms to measure the mass of

   a) a refrigerator _____

   b) a can of soup _____

5. Which is larger: a millilitre or a litre? _____

   Would you use millilitres or litres to measure the capacity of each object?

   a) a refrigerator _____

   b) a can of soup _____

Scaffolding for Lesson 5, Question 4

STUDENT BOOK PAGE 303

4. Read the rough copy you wrote for Question 3.

a) Circle the things that you like about your writing.
What makes these parts good?

_____

_____

_____

b) Revise the rough copy you wrote for Question 3 by answering these questions.

- Did you explain your thinking? I could explain my thinking better by writing

_____

_____

_____

- Did you use a model? Describe your model by describing the materials you used, the name of your shape, and the number of faces, vertices, and edges in your shape.

_____

_____

_____

- Did you use math language? What are some math words or phrases that you could use in your good copy? (For example, faces or triangle-based.)

_____

_____

_____

c) Write your good copy, using the ideas from part b).

_____

_____

_____

_____

_____

_____

Name: _____ Date: _____

3-D Shapes and 2-D Faces

Chapter 11, Lesson 1 and Curious Math

STUDENT BOOK PAGE 294–295

Lesson 1

	3-D shape	2-D faces
Name of 3-D shape	Number of edges	Total number of sides of the faces
triangle-based prism	9	18

Curious Math

3-D shape	Number of faces	Number of vertices	Number of edges

Name: _____ Date: _____

3-D Shapes Chart

Chapter 11, Lesson 2

STUDENT BOOK PAGE 296

Number of triangles/squares	Number of faces	Number of vertices	Number of faces at each vertex
3 triangles			
4 triangles			
5 triangles			
6 triangles			
7 triangles			
8 triangles			
9 triangles			
10 triangles			
4 squares			
5 squares			
6 squares			
7 squares			
8 squares			
9 squares			
10 squares			

Measuring Mass

Chapter 11 Lesson 6

STUDENT BOOK PAGE 305

List of Food and Clothing

Food

water 1 L	1 kg
salt	5 g
garlic salt	5 g
basil	5 g
curry	5 g
crackers	220 g
peanut butter	250 g
loaf of bread	675 g
pasta dinner	200 g
cereal	50 g
can of milk	625 g
cold pack	345 g
hot dog buns	675 g
hot dogs	450 g
beef jerky	175 g
chilli	525 g

can of beans	680 g
can of soup	640 g
rice	165 g
granola bars (6)	170 g
rice cakes	150 g
seeds and nuts	75 g
can of mangos	720 g
box of cookies	1400 g
animal crackers	225 g
apples	215 g
apple sauce	113 g

Clothing

jeans	850 g
towel	378 g
T-shirt	62 g
sweatshirt	130 g

Sort the items in the list by mass

0 g to 249 g	250 g to 499 g	500 g to 749 g	750 g to 1 kg

Chapter 11: Answers

Problems of the Week p. 3

1. Students' answers will vary depending on the shapes they choose. Ensure they are clear in the difference between vertices, edges, and faces and encourage them to use math language to describe the attributes of the shape.

2. Students' answers will vary. Most schools will either be a collection of rectangle-based prisms, or a rectangle-based prism, with a rectangle-based pyramid (the roof) on top.

3. Students could either estimate or weigh the objects in their desk. Encourage them to use appropriate math language in their writing.

Mental Math Master pp. 63–64

1. **a)** 36, 45, 54, **b)** 100, 125, 150 **c)** 35, 30, 25 **d)** 36, 27, 18 **e)** 16, 32, 64 **f)** 8, 4, 2
2. **a)** 60 cm **b)** 90 cm **c)** 50 cm
3. **a)** 50 cm^2 **b)** 80 cm^2 **c)** 40 cm^2 **d)** 170 cm^2 **e)** 340 cm^2
4. **a)** 1000 cm **b)** 500 cm **c)** 900 cm
5. **a)** 100 cm^2 **b)** 600 cm^2 **c)** 40 cm **d)** 1800 cm^2
6. **a)** 400 g **b)** 40 g **c)** 51 g **d)** 100 g
7. **a)** 500 mL **b)** 750 mL **c)** 75 mL **d)** 102 mL
8. **a)** 400 mL **b)** 100 g **c)** 500 g **d)** 550 mL
9. **a)** 27 cubes **b)** 175 cubes **c)** 100 cubes **d)** 200 cubes

Chapter 11 Test pp. 65–66

1. **a)** a square-based pyramid or a triangle-based prism

   b)

   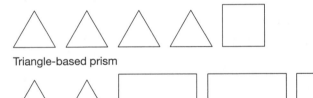

   c) square-based pyramid—8 edges; triangle-based prism—9 edges
2. **a)** cube (square-based prism) or rectangle-based prism

   b) square-based pyramid
3. **a)** 6 **b)** 9 **c)** 15 **d)** 12
4.

5. This is a square-based pyramid. It has 5 vertices, 8 edges, and 5 faces. The shape is made of 4 congruent triangle faces and one square base.

6. For example, 1 L water, apple, orange, animals crackers, sweatshirt.

7. 1 L pot

8. **a)** litres **b)** millilitres **c)** kilograms **d)** grams **e)** grams **f)** millilitres

9. 30 cubes

Chapter Task (Master) pp. 67–68

Student responses will vary significantly depending on the Cube Creature created. The following sample answer is based on the creature drawn on Student Book p. 318.

Possible response:

The arms are congruent.

- 2 arms and 2 legs
- 1 head
- 1 long body
- 2 antennae

Top View of Cube Creature

			1	1	3
		3	1	1	3
			1	1	
			1	1	
		3	1	1	3
		4	1	1	4

Details:

Arms: 1 cube by, 2 cubes by, 3 cubes + 1 cube on top of each front arm for the antennae

- Volume of each arm is 7 cubes

Head: 4 cubes attached to the 3rd layer of each arm

- Volume of head is 4 cubes

Body: 8 cubes level with the head

- Volume of body is 8 cubes

One leg: 1 cube by, 2 cubes by, 3 cubes = 6 cubes

Other leg: 3 cubes

Total Cube Creature volume is 35 cubes

Mass = 152 g

Scaffolding for Getting Started Activity Master p. 69

A. – D. Students' answers will vary depending on the packages they choose. Encourage students to use math language and review the terms shown in the illustration on page 292 if necessary.

Scaffolding for Do You Remember? Master p. 70

1. **a)** A   **b)** D   **c)** C   **d)** B
2. C and D

3.

3-D shape	Number of faces	Number of edges	Number of vertices
rectangle-based prism	6	12	8
a triangle-based pyramid	4	6	4

4. **a)** kilograms
   b) kilograms
   c) grams

5. a litre
   a) litres
   b) millilitres

Scaffolding for Lesson 5 Master p. 71

4. Students' answers will vary depending on the shapes they choose. Ensure that they use math language to describe the attributes of their shape.